The mystery letter is used only once in the picture.
Circle the mystery letter in the picture.
Cross off the letters in the box to help you keep track.

| a | b | c | d | e | f |

|

MYSTERY NUMBER

The mystery number is used only once in the picture.
Circle the mystery number in the picture.
Cross off the numbers in the box to help you keep track.

| 1 | 2 | 3 | 4 | 5 | 6 |

WHICH IS IT?

Write the names of the toys on the left.
Write the names of the animals on the right.

cat ball cow top dog doll

Toys	Animals
_____	_____
_____	_____
_____	_____
_____	_____

Compare pictures A and B.
Circle 9 things that are different in picture B.
Color the pictures.

Picture A

Picture B

Compare pictures A and B.
Circle 9 things that are different in picture B.
Color the pictures.

Picture A   **Picture B**

Compare pictures A and B.
Circle 9 things that are different in picture B.
Color the pictures.

Picture A

Picture B

Look at the word box.
Circle the words in the puzzle.

SAW BEE PIE JET CAR BED

```
U  K  B  N  M  B  S  D  Y
T (S  A  W) F  E  K  H  P
Q  M  F  D  L  D  J  G  M
Y  F  Z  O  F  W  B  H  J
K  L  V  Q  Z  L  E  W  P
F  P  I  E  W  G  E  F  B
X  K  W  B  F  Q  U  J  N
J  W  C  A  R  W  T  E  S
A  U  Y  W  M  K  L  T  O
```

BOUNTIFUL BUTTERFLIES

Both pictures have butterflies. Which butterflies are the same? Circle them.

8

POND PALS

Circle the two frogs that are the same.

Write the first letter of each picture's name.
Read the animal's name.

1. ___ ___ ___ ___

2. ___ ___ ___ ___ ___

3. ___ ___ ___ ___ ___ ___

4. ___ ___ ___ ___ ___ ___ ___

Write the first letter of each picture's name.
Read the animal's name.

1. ____ ____ ____

2. ____ ____ ____

3. ____ ____ ____ ____

4. ____ ____ ____ ____

Write the **short a** words for the pictures.

 Short a sound: **apple**

| fan bat pan hat |

1.

_____

2.

_____

3.

_____

4.

_____

5. Write **ad** to make **short a** words.

h_____   m_____   s_____

6. Write **an** to make **short a** words.

m_____   r_____   c_____

12

Read the **short a** words in the word box.

at as cat fan am ant an had

1. Write the **short a** words that have two letters.

_____   _____   _____   _____

_____   _____   _____   _____

2. Write the **short a** words that have three letters.

_____   _____   _____   _____

_____   _____   _____   _____

Spell **short a** words by writing the **short a** endings.

3. ___ **at** ___

b ___ ___

h ___ ___

m ___ ___

p ___ ___

4. ___ **am** ___

h ___ ___

j ___ ___

S ___ ___

r ___ ___

5. ___ **an** ___

r ___ ___

m ___ ___

p ___ ___

f ___ ___

Color the **short e** words **blue**.

Short e sound: **nest**

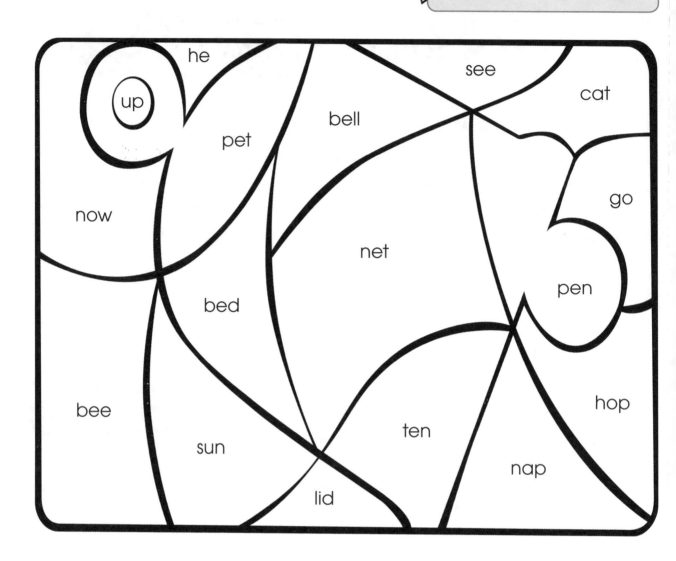

1. Write **et** to make **short e** words.

n _____   p _____   j _____

2. Write **en** to make **short e** words.

h _____   m _____   t _____

14

Write the **short e** words to answer the riddles.

| ten   bell   red   sled   nest   bed |

_____

1. We ride on it when there is snow. _____

_____

2. It makes a ringing sound. _____

_____

3. Fire trucks are often this color. _____

_____

4. A dime is this many pennies. _____

_____

5. We sleep on it. _____

_____

6. Baby birds stay in it. _____

Which **short i** words go with the pictures?
Hint: They are opposites of "out" and "hers."

 **Short i** sound: **igloo**

| big dig in pig wig his |

1.

out

2.

hers

3. Write the **short i** words that end with **ig**.

_____   _____

_____   _____

_____   _____

Write **i** to make **short i** words and to finish the silly sentences.
Read the sentences to a friend.

1. I h____d a l____d, I d____d.

2. I w____ll f____ll a h____ll with flowers.

3. The b____g p____g ate a f____g.

4. I w____sh the f____sh were still on the d____sh.

Write the missing letters to make the **short i** words from the sentences above.

5. ____id
____id
____id

6. ____ill
____ill
____ill

7. ____ig
____ig
____ig

8. ____ish
____ish
____ish

Write the **short o** words for the pictures. **Short o** sound: **octopus**

| hot doll not fox tot box |

1.

_____

- - - - - - - - - - - - - - - - - -

_____

2.

_____

- - - - - - - - - - - - - - - - - -

_____

3. Write the **short o** words that end with **t**.

_____   _____   _____

- - - - - - - - - - -   - - - - - - - - - - -   - - - - - - - - - -

_____   _____   _____

4. Write the **short o** word that rhymes with **fox**.

_____

- - - - - - - - - - - - -

_____

Write the **short o** words to answer the riddles.

rock box sock dock lock clock

1. It tells you the time.

   _____

   _____

2. A key opens it.

   _____

   _____

3. You wear it on your foot.

   _____

   _____

4. You put things in it.

   _____

   _____

5. A boat can be here.

   _____

   _____

6. It is hard.

   _____

   _____

Write the first letter of each picture's name to spell the **short u** words.

bug gum hug cup fun mud sun pup

1. ___ + ___ + ___ ___ ___ ___

2. ___ + ___ + ___ ___ ___ ___

3. ___ + ___ + ___ ___ ___ ___

4. ___ + ___ + ___ ___ ___ ___

5. ___ + ___ + ___ ___ ___ ___

6. ___ + ___ + ___ ___ ___ ___

7. ___ + ___ + ___ ___ ___ ___

8. ___ + ___ + ___ ___ ___ ___

SHORT VOWELS: A, E, I, O, U

Finish the words by filling in the missing vowels. Each word has the same short vowel sound as the picture.

short u words

s__n
b__s

short a words

c_a_t
m_a_n

short e words

h__n
r__d

short o words

t__p
h__p

short i words

p__g
b__g

Use the clues to solve the puzzle.

sun egg pig sock ten hat

1.

2. s o c k

3. 4.

5.

Across ⟷

2. Which word has the same vowel sound as "dock"?
3. Which word rhymes with "men"?
5. Which word has the same vowel sound as "dig"?

Down ⬇

1. Which word has the same vowel sound as "sat"?
2. Which word has the same vowel sound as "fun"?
4. Which word has the same vowel sound as "leg"?

DIVINE D WORDS

Look at the word box.
Find each word in the puzzle.

DOG DAD DRUM DUCK DOLL DISH DAY

```
Q W R T U P B F D
O D B M L J D M O
W O X D P W D J L
R G Q A B S R Z L
P T W Y S H U K P
M D U C K X M X J
G Q W M N F R P K
S Y G D J D A D B
B D I S H H K C F
```

Look at the word box.
Find each word in the puzzle.

HAT   HORN   HAM   HOOK   HOUSE   HEART   HEN

E H O R N G F L H
P K S N X Q P X A
H G C H O O K N T
A B K Z M Q R T Q
M J H E A R T V K
W Z W P R T B K C
K R Q D Q K N H M
P H O U S E R E T
Z T P J N K B N Q

LONG A

Write the **long a** words to answer the riddles.

rake game tape vase cake gate

1. You can put flowers in me.
   What am I?

_____

2. You like to eat me.
   What am I?

_____

3. I fix a torn page.
   What am I?

_____

4. You use me to pile leaves.
   What am I?

_____

5. Write the **long a** words that begin with **g**.

_____   _____

Use the clues to solve the puzzle.

Long e sound: **bee**

dream clean money bean leave tree key seed see

Across ⟨⟷⟩

2. Produces a plant
5. Go away
7. Used to buy things
8. A kind of vegetable

Down ⬇

1. A large plant
2. Look at
3. Happens when asleep
4. Opposite of dirty
6. Opens a lock

Write the **long e** words to answer the riddles.

bee seal me tree he leaf

1. I can swim.
   What am I?

_____

2. I am a large plant.
   What am I?

_____

3. I grow on a tree.
   What am I?

_____

4. I get food from flowers.
   What am I?

_____

5. Write the two-letter **long e** words.

_____

_____

Write the **long i** words to answer the riddles.

 Long i sound: **pie**

kite tie fine bike like ride

1. You can fly me.
   What am I?

_____

2. You can ride me.
   What am I?

_____

3. I am something to wear.
   What am I?

_____

Write the **long i** words that fit these shapes.

4.

5.

6.

kind find try night cry right

1. Write the **long i** words that end with **d**.

_____   _____

_____   _____

_____   _____

2. Write the **long i** words that rhyme with **kite**.

_____   _____

_____   _____

_____   _____

3. Write the **long i** words that end with **y**.

_____   _____

_____   _____

_____   _____

4. Underline the **long i** words in the story.

My friend and I took a hike up a hill.
We flew our kites high in the sky.
My friend and I had a fun time.

Write the **long o** words to finish the sentences. **Long o** sound: **rose**

---

show hold boat told grow goat note home

_____

1. What did the _____ say?

_____

2. The _____ sailed across the lake.

_____

3. Who _____ you the joke?

Mom,
I went to Brenda's to play. I will be home at 4:30.
Love,
    Sue

_____

4. How high will the tree _____?

_____

5. We saw a good _____ on TV last night.

_____

6. The _____ has horns.

_____

7. It is time to go _____.

_____

8. Please _____ my hand.

Write the **long o** words for the clues.
Then read the letters in the box to answer the riddle.

| own told slow bow coat grow goat |

1. get bigger

2. worn over clothes

3. not fast

4. a knot with two loops

5. have

6. a farm animal

7. said; put into words

I float on water. What am I? _a_____

Use the code to write the **long u** words.

Long u sound: **unicorn**

c	e	g	h	l	r	t	u	b
△	○	☆	◇	<	>	○	□	▯

cube cute huge
rule mule tube

1. △ □ ○ ○ _____

2. ○ □ ▯ ○ _____

3. ◇ □ ☆ ○ _____

4. > □ < ○ _____

Write the **long u** words for the pictures.

5. _____

6. _____

LONG U

Write the words with a **long u** sound to finish the sentences.

true clue cute huge blue use

_____

1. To solve the mystery, they needed the final _____.

_____

2. If it is not false, it is _____.

_____

3. I thought the baby was very _____.

_____

4. An elephant is a _____ animal.

_____

5. The sky is the color _____.

_____

6. When you work with something, you _____ it.

GO LONG!

Use the clues to solve the puzzle.

kite tube bee bone slide rake

 Across ⟨⟷⟩

1. This word has the **long a** sound.
4. This word has the **long u** sound.
6. This word has the **long i** sound and five letters.

 Down ⬇

2. This word has the **long i** sound and 4 letters.
3. This word has the **long e** sound.
5. This word has the **long o** sound.

34

LONG VOWEL SOUNDS

Say the words.
Circle the words that have the long vowel sound.

1.

a

cake   ant   baby   cat

2.

e

bear   bee   tree   pet

3.

i

pig   kite   ring   tie

4.

o

boat   rope   dog   fox

5.

u

rug   sun   tube   blue

COLORFUL SEA OF VOWELS

Color the fish that have a long vowel sound orange.
Color the fish that have a short vowel sound green.
Help the squid get to her cave.
Draw a line to connect the fish
that have a long vowel sound.

dish

fish

fin

me

bat

crab

huge

whale

hot

sea

ten

home

swim

hug

bite

Many words that are spelled **consonant-vowel-consonant-e** have a long vowel sound.

Write the letter **e** to make long vowel words.

1. man____

2. kit____

3. pin____

4. hug____

5. dim____

6. mad____

Write the long vowel words from above to complete the sentences.

7. A whale is _____.

8. It _____ a mess.

9. It cost a _____.

10. How high can your _____ fly?

11. That is a _____ tree.

12. The horse had a black _____.

Look at the word box.
Circle the words in the puzzle.

SOCK SUN STAR SEAL SNAIL SING SOAP SIT

Q D L P J S I T V
W S F M B X Y O H
Q I J K S S T A R
C N V U N W L X M
S G P M A K J B R
E Z S Q I J S U N
A Q M P L C Q P K
L S O A P I P G K
E P F T W S O C K

Look at the word box.
Circle the words in the puzzle.

RAIN RING ROBOT ROSE RUG RED ROBIN ROPE

```
R A I N F T Y P Q
R B S Q O W R U R
I K B J P Q O K O
N H R E D Z B R B
G K L O L J O Q I
R O S E R W T P N
V R Z Q O W Z J L
Z U I F P R H N Q
I G C Q E W F C W
```

Write all the words that start with **sh** in the sheep pen.
Write all the words that end with **sh** in the fish pond.

push   shop   shoe   show   dish   shirt   shell   wash   wish

Sheep Pen

1. _____

2. _____

3. _____

4. _____

5. _____

Fish Pond

6. _____

7. _____

8. _____

9. _____

CHUMMY FRIENDS

Draw a line from each word that starts with **ch** to Chad.
Draw a line from each word that ends with **ch** to Mitch.

fish   catch

book   match

ditch   touch

Chad

glass   chair

cherry   porch

man   watch

cheese   beach

chimney   Mitch   banana

Write the correct **th** words to finish the sentences.

bath path there Thank thirty think

_____

1. Our dog, Rex, would not let us give him a _____.

_____

2. We _____ he's afraid of water.

_____

3. Rex tried to run from us, but we followed his _____.

_____

4. It took us almost _____ minutes to catch him.

_____   _____

5. _____ goodness Mom was _____ to help us!

Write the **ch**, **wh**, **sh**, and **th** words for the clues.
Then read the letters in the box to answer the riddle.

inch branch white she whale path

1. a water animal

2. the color of snow

3. part of a ruler

4. a walkway

5. opposite of he

6. part of a tree

I come after autumn. What am I? _____

Read the story.
Underline all the **oi** and **oy** words.

Roy was in a toy store with his mother. He had saved his coins to buy a new toy. There were many kinds of toys. Some toys made too much noise. Some toys cost too much. He finally made a choice. Roy counted all his coins. He chose a toy he could enjoy with his friends.

Underline the correct answers.

1. Where was Roy?

    at home   in a toy store   at school

2. Who was with Roy?

    his mother   his sister   no one

3. Write three **oi** and three **oy** words from the story.

oi	**oy**
_____	_____
_____	_____
_____	_____

A MOUSE IN THE HOUSE

Read the story.
Underline all the **ou** and **ow** words.

Mom and I saw a brown mouse in our house. Our cat saw it and gave a howl. He jumped down onto the floor and started to run. The cat chased the mouse around the house. We opened the door to let the mouse out. It let out a squeak, and away it ran.

Underline the correct answers.

1. Who saw the mouse?

   Mom and Dad   two friends   Mom and I

2. Which words rhyme?

   house   howl   mouse

3. Write three **ou** and three **ow** words from the story.

ou	ow
_____	_____
_____	_____
_____	_____

Write the words for the clues.

1. You can sit on it.

   _____

2. You go there to learn.

   _____

3. It is the color of the sky.

   _____

4. Things stick together with it.

   _____

5. If there are not many, there are _____.

   _____

6. It is the opposite of old.

   _____

new

few

stool

glue

blue

school

Write the words for the clues.

food tool new moon zoo flew soon blue

1. helps do work

2. not old

3. something to eat

4. before long

5. a color

6. seen at night

7. where animals are kept

8. rhymes with "blew"

Write **oo** or **ew** to make words.

9. | | | |
   |---|---|---|
   | s | t | |

10. | | | |
    |---|---|---|
    | m | | d |

11. | | | |
    |---|---|---|
    | c | | l |

12. | | | |
    |---|---|---|
    | r | | m |

13. | | | |
    |---|---|---|
    | b | l | |

14. | | | |
    |---|---|---|
    | k | n | |

The letters **c** and **g** make different sounds in different words. Copy the words. Say the words.

hard c sound	**soft c sound**
1. The letter **c** sounds like **k** before these vowels: **a**, **o**, and **u**.	2. The letter **c** sounds like **s** before these vowels: **i** and **e**.
cat	city
cow	circus
cup	cent

hard g sound	**soft g sound**
3. The letter **g** sounds like the **g** in **goat** before these vowels: **a**, **o**, and **u**.	4. The letter **g** usually sounds like **j** before these vowels: **i** and **e**.
gas	general
gum	gentle
good	giraffe

RHYME TIME

Words that **rhyme** have the same vowel sound and ending sound.

Underline the rhyming words.

1. The king began to sing.

2. Her cat wears a hat.

3. The dog ran after the frog.

4. I wish I had a fish.

5. My coat is in the boat.

6. A vet took care of my pet.

Underline the rhyming words.

1. The pail fell in the well.

2. Look at my new book.

3. The boy had a new toy.

4. I like your new bike.

5. I was told you had a cold.

6. The pig wore a wig.

RHYMING WORD SEARCH

Look at the word box.
Circle the words in the puzzle.

> CAT   HAT   KING   RING   BOAT   COAT   DOG   FROG

```
K  C  A  T  O  H  A  T  G
B  R  T  X  K  O  P  T  C
K  K  T  B  O  A  T  L  O
Q  I  N  P  U  V  K  P  A
Y  N  Z  A  S  J  S  T  T
O  G  T  R  I  N  G  Q  E
L  N  W  D  Z  O  I  E  D
R  T  F  R  O  G  K  J  O
C  Z  T  D  W  Y  S  M  G
```

RHYMING CLUES

Read the clues.
Write the correct rhyming words.

1. It is the opposite of cold.
   It rhymes with "not."

   _____

   _____

2. It is a pet.
   It rhymes with "jog."

   _____

   _____

3. You wear one on your foot.
   It rhymes with "rock."

   _____

   _____

4. It is a wild animal.
   It rhymes with "box."

   _____

   _____

5. It tells the time.
   It rhymes with "block."

   _____

   _____

RHYMING CLUES

Read the clues.
Write the correct rhyming words.

1. You sleep on it.
   It rhymes with "red."

   _____

   _____

2. It can swim.
   It rhymes with "dish."

   _____

   _____

3. You sail about on it.
   It rhymes with "take."

   _____

   _____

4. It is something to wear in winter.
   It rhymes with "boat."

   _____

   _____

5. It rings.
   It rhymes with "tell."

   _____

   _____

Read the clues.
Write the correct rhyming words.

1. You can ride it.
   It rhymes with "like."
   _____

   _____

2. It is worth 10¢.
   It rhymes with "time."
   _____

   _____

3. It is something you fly.
   It rhymes with "white."
   _____

   _____

4. It is the opposite of "day."
   It rhymes with "right."
   _____

   _____

5. It is a sweet dessert.
   It rhymes with "tie."
   _____

   _____

6. You do it when you are sad.
   It rhymes with "dry."
   _____

   _____

RHYMING CLUES

Read the clues.
Write the correct rhyming words.

1. You see this in the sky at night.
   It rhymes with "soon."

   _____

2. Bees make this in their hive.
   It rhymes with "money."

   _____

3. This animal eats cheese.
   It rhymes with "house."

   _____

4. This animal makes the milk we drink.
   It rhymes with "now."

   _____

5. This thing sails on water.
   It rhymes with "coat."

   _____

6. This is something you read.
   It rhymes with "look."

   _____

Read the poems.
Write the correct rhyming word from the
word box to complete each poem.

day round spring

1. I like the flowers growing.
   I like the birds that sing.
   I like the growing season.
   We call that season _____.

   _____

2. I like sunny days with
   Snow on the ground.
   I like the nights when
   The moon is so _____.

   _____

3. Some days are foggy.
   Some days are gray.
   I like the times when it's
   Sunny all _____.

   _____

RHYMING POEMS

Read the poems.
Write the correct rhyming word from the
word box to complete each poem.

| white   snow   running   showers |

1. Clouds fly high
   When the sun is bright.
   The very best clouds
   Are fluffy and _____.

   _____
   - - - - - - - - - - - - - - - -
   _____

2. The hot days are best
   For swimming and sunning.
   But the cool days are better
   When I want to go _____.

   _____
   - - - - - - - - - - - - - - - -
   _____

3. It falls from the sky
   When the cold winds blow.
   I hope it stays!
   I want to play in the _____.

   _____
   - - - - - - - - - - - - - - - -
   _____

4. April brings rain.
   May brings flowers.
   The colors in May
   Make me like April _____.

   _____
   - - - - - - - - - - - - - - - -
   _____

Use the clues to solve the puzzle.

smile sting dress class smell drag

Across ⟷

2. I rhyme with "thing."
4. I rhyme with "mile."
5. I rhyme with "mess."

Down ⬇

1. I rhyme with "flag."
2. I rhyme with "tell."
3. I rhyme with "grass."

CROSSWORD RHYMES

Use the clues to solve the puzzle.

true trap truck tree trip trick

Across ⟷

2. What rhymes with "slip"?
3. What rhymes with "luck"?
4. What rhymes with "bee"?

Down ⬇

1. What rhymes with "clap"?
2. What rhymes with "stick"?
3. What rhymes with "blue"?

Happy is the **opposite** of sad.

Draw a line between the opposites.

 in

night

day

out

hot

cold

old

new

Draw a line between the opposites.

 big

 fast

 wet

 run

 on

 little

 walk

 off

 slow

 dry

Draw a line between the opposites.

stop

up

short

high

over

low

tall

under

go

down

OPPOSITES WORD SEARCH

Look at the word box.
Circle the words in the puzzle.

STOP   GO   ON   OFF   WET   DRY   HOT   COLD   UP   DOWN

```
V  B  T  G  W  E  T  R  L
S  P  K  Z  X  Q  B  H  Y
T  G  O  K  J  H  N  D  T
O  U  D  Z  Q  O  Y  R  T
P  X  Z  O  N  T  S  Y  L
N  S  U  F  F  X  Q  B  R
W  G  J  F  L  C  O  L  D
N  F  S  S  T  Z  W  J  Y
S  U  P  Y  D  O  W  N  Z
```

OPPOSITES WORD SEARCH

Look at the word box.
Circle the words in the puzzle.

BIG LITTLE FAST SLOW NEW OLD IN OUT

V	B	I	G	Z	I	N	E	L
O	Z	Q	T	X	Q	B	H	I
U	G	L	N	E	W	N	P	T
T	U	Q	B	N	P	Y	O	T
K	X	O	L	D	R	S	K	L
N	S	U	Q	F	X	L	B	E
A	Q	J	D	L	K	O	X	J
N	F	A	S	T	Z	W	J	Y
Z	P	S	M	N	G	E	B	Z

COMPOUND WORDS

A **compound word** is a new word made out of two words that are joined together.

sun + shine = sunshine

Look at the pictures.
Write the compound words.

cupcake baseball butterfly birdhouse rainbow football

1. +   _____

2. + _____

3. +   _____

4. +   _____

5. + _____

6. + _____

Look at the pictures.
Write the compound words.

> **sunflower starfish firefly skateboard
> rattlesnake basketball doghouse**

1. 🐕 + 🏠 _____

2. 🔥 + 🪰 _____

3. 🧺 + ⚪ _____

4. ⭐ + 🐟 _____

5. 🪀 + 🐍 _____

6. ☀️ + 🌸 _____

7. 👟 + ▬ _____

CONTRACTIONS

A **contraction** is two words put together.

An **apostrophe** (') shows where there is a missing letter or letters.

do + n**o**t = don't
we + **wi**ll = we'll

Write contractions for the underlined words.

| haven't don't Let's isn't   shouldn't we'll |

_____

1. Please <u>do not</u> go. _____

_____

2. The job <u>is not</u> done. _____

_____

3. We <u>have not</u> painted it. _____

_____

4. <u>Let us</u> paint it red. _____

_____

5. It <u>should not</u> take long. _____

_____

6. Then <u>we will</u> go home. _____

CONTRACTIONS

Combine the words to make contractions.

| can't | it's | he'd | aren't | isn't | I'm | couldn't | we'll |
| she's | we're | don't | they're | doesn't | wouldn't |

1. does + not = _____

2. is + not = _____

3. they + are = _____

4. she + is = _____

5. can + not = _____

6. are + not = _____

7. I + am = _____

8. we + are = _____

9. do + not = _____

10. could + not = _____

11. he + would = _____

12. we + will = _____

13. would + not = _____

14. it + is = _____

SYNONYMS

Synonyms are words that mean the same thing.

Happy means the same as **glad**.
Laugh means the same as **giggle**.

Draw a line between the synonyms.

fast	large
tiny	a few
take	slide
some	shove
slip	grab
big	quick
push	small

ANTONYMS

Antonyms are words that are **opposites**.

On is the opposite of **off**.
Up is the opposite of **down**.

Draw a line between the antonyms.

give	slow
after	small
large	before
old	none
fast	take
all	new
hot	over
under	cold

HOMOPHONES

Homophones are words that sound alike but are spelled differently. They also have different meanings.

Write the correct homophones to finish the sentences.

1. Give the toy _____ the baby.

   to   two

2. Put the book over _____.

   their   there

3. I cannot _____ her.

   hear   here

4. Who _____ the game?

   won   one

5. Is your answer _____?

   write   right

6. Jan _____ the apple.

   eight   ate

Use the clues to solve the puzzle.

horse pig sheep goose goat cat

Across ⟨⟷⟩

2. Which animal gives us wool?
5. Which animal has feathers?
6. Which animal likes to chase mice?

Down ⬇

1. Which animal do we ride?
3. Which animal likes to roll in mud?
4. Which animal has horns?

Read the sentences.
Circle the correct answers.

1. The clown wears a silly hat.

   yes   no

2. He has a red nose.

   yes   no

3. He has little shoes.

   yes   no

4. He wears a yellow coat.

   yes   no

5. He has two green balls.

   yes   no

6. He rides a bike.

   yes   no

THE MAGICIAN

Read the sentences.
Circle the correct answers.

1. The magician is wearing a tall hat.

   yes   no

2. He is wearing a purple cape.

   yes   no

3. He has a magic wand.

   yes   no

4. He is wearing a red tie.

   yes   no

5. He has little shoes.

   yes   no

6. There is a rabbit in his hat.

   yes   no

Read the sentences and questions.
Write the correct answers.

| birds chickens ducks frogs dogs |

1. Cows do not bark. Which animals bark?
   _____
   _____
   _____

2. Chickens do not quack. Which animals quack?
   _____
   _____
   _____

3. Dogs do not lay eggs. Which animals lay eggs?
   _____
   _____
   _____

4. Pigs do not hop. Which animals hop?
   _____
   _____
   _____

5. Cats do not fly. Which animals fly?
   _____
   _____
   _____

Read the clues.
Write the names under the correct pictures.

1. Henry keeps the homes of the animals clean.
2. Liz helps sick animals.
3. Chan works with the sea animals.
4. Beth feeds hungry animals.

_____

_____

_____

_____

WHO'S WHO?

Read the clues.
Write the names under the correct pictures.

1. Sarah has a green hat.
2. Mia always wears red.
3. Ken never wears blue.
4. Ty has purple shoes.
5. Mimi likes to paint.

_____

_____

_____

_____

_____

_____

_____

_____

_____

_____

Read the clues.
Write the names under the correct pictures.

1. Jill plays the violin.
2. Zeke plays baseball.
3. Jessie likes to swim.
4. Peter plays soccer.
5. Adam makes things.

Read the clues to find the correct answers.

I. Jenny's cat is orange.
He is wearing a blue collar.
Circle Jenny's cat.

2. Jack's dog is standing.
She has spots.
Circle Jack's dog.

3. The bird's name ends with **y**.
It has five letters.
Circle the bird's name.

Ginger   Billy

Chipper   Shelly

AFTER SCHOOL FUN

Read the clues to solve the problems.
Write the names under the correct pictures.

1. Alexis, Ted, and Kelly had a race.
   Ted came in last place.
   Alexis did not win.

_____   _____   _____

_____

Who won the race? _____

---

2. John, David, and Becky live in these houses.
   John does not live next to David.
   David's house is next to the street sign.

_____   _____   _____

_____

Who lives in the middle house? _____

THE SILLY MAN

Read the poem. Circle the answers to the questions.

I know a silly man who walks on his hands.
He has a silly car. It doesn't go far.
In his silly town, shops are upside down.
Tell me if you can, when you see this silly man.

1. Which is the silly man?

2. Which car is his?

3. Which hat is his?

4. Which pet is his?

Use the clues to solve the puzzle.

toast boat gold goat hole note

Across ⟷

2. made with bread
4. an animal
6. short letter

Down ↓

1. moves in water
3. an empty space
5. a yellow metal

ANIMAL FACTS

Use the code to answer the questions.

Code

P	O	S	F	Y	N	I	L	T	E	G	W	R	A
1	2	3	4	5	6	7	8	9	10	11	12	13	14

1. Which animal travels on one big foot?

   ___ ___ ___ ___ ___

   The ___ ___ ___ ___ ___
         3   6   14   7   8

2. Which wild dog is the largest?

   ___ ___ ___ ___   ___ ___ ___ ___

   The ___ ___ ___ ___   ___ ___ ___ ___
        11   13   14   5   12   2   8   4

3. Which bird can be taught to use words?

   ___ ___ ___ ___ ___ ___

   The ___ ___ ___ ___ ___ ___
       1   14   13   13   2   9

Write each problem's number in the box by the correct animal.

WORD SOUNDS

Syllables are sounds that make up words.

Say each word slowly.
Circle how many parts of the word you hear.

kite

① 2

apple

1 ②

---

1. snowflake

1   2

carrot

1   2

leaf

1   2

2. sock

1   2

suitcase

1   2

penguin

1   2

3. pear

1   2

cake

1   2

igloo

1   2

1. **mouse**

1   2

gift

1   2

taco

1   2

2. **cup**

1   2

popcorn

1   2

shirt

1   2

3. **seahorse**

1   2

insect

1   2

pie

1   2

4. **cat**

1   2

balloon

1   2

lemon

1   2

Use the clues to solve the puzzle.

letter bird turn mother word hurt work

Across ⟷

3. to move around a center
4. to do harm
5. something that is said
6. an animal with wings and feathers

Down ⬇

1. a note written to a person
2. a female parent
5. job

ORDER UP!

Alphabetical order is a way of arranging words to follow the same sequence as the letters in the alphabet.
Use the first letters of the words to put them in alphabetical order.

ant   **c**at   **p**ig

The words **dig**, **dog**, and **day** begin with the same first letter.
Use their second letters to put them in alphabetical order.

d**a**y   d**i**g   d**o**g

Put the names of these friends in alphabetical order.
Remember! Names always begin with an uppercase letter.

1. Lucy, Tina, Beth

2. Peter, Matt, Jamie

3. Amy, Abby, Anna

4. David, Drew, Doug

Extra Credit!

5. Write the letters of your name. Then write the letters in ABC order.

Circle **yes** if the sentence is true or circle **no** if it is not true. Circle the letter next to each of your answers. Then write the circled letters in order to answer the riddle.

			yes		no	
1.	All birds have feathers.		yes	y	no	g
2.	All living things need food.		yes	a	no	l
3.	Insects have bones.		yes	w	no	r
4.	Ice is frozen water.		yes	d	no	f
5.	Trees are large plants.		yes	s	no	r
6.	Plants need water to grow.		yes	t	no	s
7.	The world's largest animal is the giraffe.		yes	v	no	i
8.	The earth is flat.		yes	i	no	c
9.	A plant is alive.		yes	k	no	x

What has a foot on each side and one in the middle?

A ___ ___ ___ ___ ___ ___ ___ ___ ___

HELP FOR A SICK PIG

Circle **yes** if the sentence is true or circle **no** if it is not true. Circle the letter next to each of your answers. Then write the circled letters in order to answer the riddle.

			yes		no	
1.	Celery is a vegetable.		yes	o	no	g
2.	Birds fly.		yes	i	no	j
3.	The letters **a**, **e**, **i**, **o**, and **u** are consonants.		yes	s	no	n
4.	**Each**, **eat**, and **bead** have the **long a** sound.		yes	w	no	k
5.	**Happy** is the opposite of **sad**.		yes	m	no	r
6.	Bees make honey.		yes	e	no	l
7.	**Same** is a synonym of **different**.		yes	k	no	n
8.	**King** and **ring** are rhyming words.		yes	t	no	q

What do you give sick pigs?

_____ _____ _____ _____ _____ _____ _____

_____ _____ _____ _____ _____

Find the words that go together.
Look across, down, and diagonally.

1

gate	over	snip
gave	under	chain
ripe	above	chair

2

baseball	smaller	found
tallest	soccer	happy
bumpy	short	football

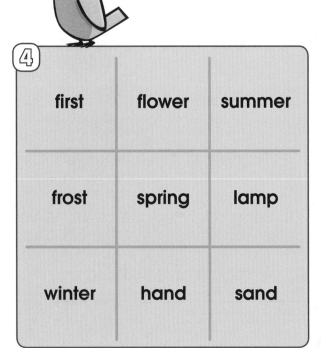

3

cloud	hilly	rain
claw	beak	wing
hose	nose	coin

4

first	flower	summer
frost	spring	lamp
winter	hand	sand

TIC-TAC-TOE

Find the words that go together.
Look across, down, and diagonally.

1

fish	key	five
bug	jump	four
star	blue	two

2

ball	rain	bat
lemon	butterfly	green
robin	down	red

3

sun	big	goat
wet	rain	two
star	old	snow

4

rose	ant	red
fox	bus	ten
dollar	penny	nickel

Find the words that go together.
Look across, down, and diagonally.

1

bee	ant	fly
seal	hat	frog
house	ball	blue

2

yo-yo	bird	one
hand	ball	hill
soap	gate	doll

3

drum	owl	lizard
wolf	apple	turtle
boot	crab	snake

4

snow	bat	train
pear	car	gold
jet	robin	dog

BIRTHDAY PARTY

Write 1 by what happens first.
Write 2 by what happens next.
Write 3 by what happens last.

A GROWING TOMATO PLANT

Number the pictures from 1 to 6 to show the correct order.

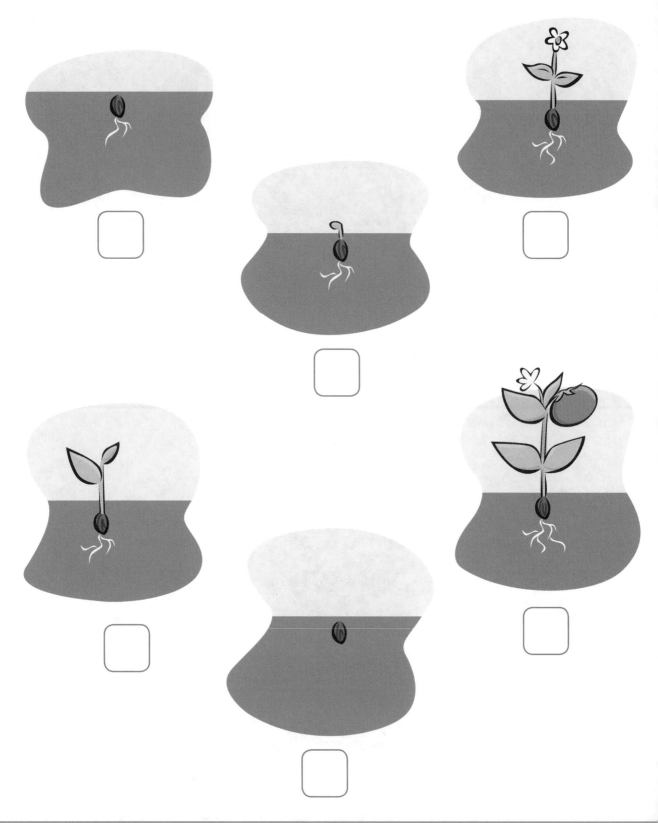

MAKING A CLEVER MASK

Number the pictures from 1 to 6 to show the correct order.

OH CHRISTMAS TREE!

Number the pictures from 1 to 6 to show the correct order.

Write 1 by what happens first.
Write 2 by what happens next.
Write 3 by what happens last.

1. Write what happened at the beginning.

_____

_____

2. Write what happened in the middle.

_____

_____

3. Write what happened at the end.

_____

_____

_____

_____

GOING SLEDDING

Write 1 by what happens first.
Write 2 by what happens next.
Write 3 by what happens last.

1. Write what happened at the beginning.

2. Write what happened in the middle.

3. Write what happened at the end.

Read the stories.
Number the pictures from 1 to 3 to show the correct order.

1. Tracy pulls her wagon.
She finds a kitten.
Tracy gives the kitten a ride.

_____ _____ _____

2. Tom has an old wagon.
"I will paint my wagon," says Tom.
So he paints his wagon.

_____ _____ _____

3. The kitten wants to eat.
It waits for food.
At last, the kitten eats.

_____ _____ _____

Read the stories.
Number the pictures from 1 to 3 to show the correct order.

1. The duck went to a party.
   The duck ate some cake.
   The duck went home.

___ ___ ___

2. Mom made a cake.
   I ate a piece.
   Then I went to bed.

___ ___ ___

3. Jane sees a duck.
   The duck sees Jane.
   Then the duck walks up to Jane.

___ ___ ___

CYCLE OF AN APPLE TREE

Here is the life cycle of an apple tree:

seed

tree

tree produces blossoms

tree's blossoms become fruit

fruit

Write the missing words.

1. A tree begins as a _____.

2. Next, the seed becomes a _____.

3. An older tree makes _____.

4. The blossoms become _____.

5. Inside the fruit are _____.

RUB-A-DUB-DUB!

Josh and Dani planned a neighborhood dog wash.
Read the sentences. Draw a line to show where they go.

1. First, they go to Mrs. Green's.
2. Next, they go to Mr. Berry's.
3. After that, they go to the Ride's house.
4. Last, they go to Mrs. Ball's.

Rub-a-dub-dub,
Washing dogs in a tub.   _____
Rub-a-dub-dub,
How many dogs did they scrub? _____ dogs

A frog goes through five stages during its life cycle:

1   2   3   4   5

Number the sentences from 1 to 5 to show the correct order.

_____ Froggy is a tiny tadpole.

_____ Froggy is a big frog.

_____ Froggy is an egg.

_____ Froggy grows four legs.

_____ Froggy grows two legs.

Read the story.

The night was dark.
Tina heard something go, "Whooo!"
Tina was scared.
The window blew open.
Tina saw an owl.
The owl went, "Whooo!"
Tina was not scared then.

Number the sentences from
1 to 4 to show the correct order.

_____ The window blew open.

_____ Tina saw an owl.

_____ Tina was scared.

_____ Tina was not scared then.

TOMATO GARDEN

Read the directions.

Find a place that is sunny.
Dig a hole.
Set the tomato plant in the hole.
Pat dirt around the plant.
Water the plant often.
When the tomatoes are ripe, enjoy!

Number the sentences from
1 to 5 to show the correct order.

_____

_____ Set the tomato plant in the hole.

_____

_____ Find a place that is sunny.

_____

_____ Pat dirt around the plant.

_____

_____ Water the plant often.

_____

_____ Dig a hole.

HALLOWEEN PARTY

Can you guess what will happen next?

John received an invitation to a Halloween party. He went to his dad's closet and found some old clothes for his costume. After that, John arrived at the Halloween party.

1. Write a sentence that tells what will happen next.

_____

- -

_____

- -

_____

2. Write a sentence that tells why John went to the Halloween party.

_____

- -

_____

- -

_____

GETTING SOME MILK

Can you guess what will happen next?

Henry was thirsty. He went to the cabinet and got a glass. Then he opened the refrigerator. Next, he got some milk. Henry poured the milk into the glass.

1. Write a sentence that tells what Henry will do next.

_____

_____

_____

2. Write a sentence that tells why Henry was thirsty.

_____

_____

_____

Real things can actually happen.
Make-believe things cannot really happen.

Circle real or make-believe.

1. The cow jumped over the moon.	real	make-believe
Jenny fed the cow hay.	real	make-believe
2. The cat looks for mice in the barn.	real	make-believe
The cat came dancing out of the barn.	real	make-believe
3. An old woman lives near us.	real	make-believe
An old woman lives in a shoe.	real	make-believe
4. Three little kittens lost their mittens.	real	make-believe
Three little kittens were lost.	real	make-believe

REALISTIC OR FANTASY?

Realistic fiction stories are about things that could really happen.
Fantasy stories are about things that could not really happen.

Realistic fiction story

Fantasy story

Write **R** in front of what could really happen.
Write **F** in front of what could not really happen.

_____ 1. The pig spread his wings and flew away.

_____ 2. The fireman rushed to put out the fire.

_____ 3. The fox had a party with the chicken.

_____ 4. Ellen scored the winning goal.

_____ 5. The dish ran away with the spoon.

_____ 6. The farmer planted gumball trees.

_____ 7. Dad rowed the boat across the river.

_____ 8. The baby played with toy animals.

FACT OR OPINION?

A **fact** is something that can be proved.

Birds have wings.
You can look at a bird or check in a book to find out whether birds have wings.

An **opinion** is something that someone believes. An opinion can't be proved.

A robin is pretty.

Circle fact or opinion.

1. Most birds can fly.   fact   opinion

2. Birds make good pets.   fact   opinion

3. Birds lay eggs.   fact   opinion

4. Owls are interesting birds.   fact   opinion

5. Robins make the best nests.   fact   opinion

6. Most birds have feathers.   fact   opinion

Extra Credit!

Write one fact about birds.
_____
- -
_____

What is your opinion about birds?
_____
- -
_____

FACT OR OPINION?

Circle **fact** or **opinion**.

1. Spiders have eight legs.   fact   opinion

2. Insects are scary.   fact   opinion

3. A tarantula would be a great pet.   fact   opinion

4. Insects have three body parts.   fact   opinion

5. Both spiders and insects shed their skin.   fact   opinion

6. Insects are better than spiders.   fact   opinion

Extra Credit!

Write one fact about spiders.
_____
- -
_____

What is your opinion about insects?
_____
- -
_____

FACT OR OPINION?

Circle **fact** or **opinion**.

1. Most ocean animals are fish.   fact   opinion

2. Fish make good pets.   fact   opinion

3. Some fish have bright colors.   fact   opinion

4. Fish are cold-blooded.   fact   opinion

5. Fishing is fun.   fact   opinion

6. Everyone should eat fish.   fact   opinion

Fish Fact
We are called
"clownfish."

Extra Credit!

Write one fact about fish.

_____

- - - - - - - - - - - - - - - - - - - -

_____

What is your opinion about fish?

_____

- - - - - - - - - - - - - - - - - - - -

_____

CALENDAR QUESTION

Use the code to solve the riddle.

Code

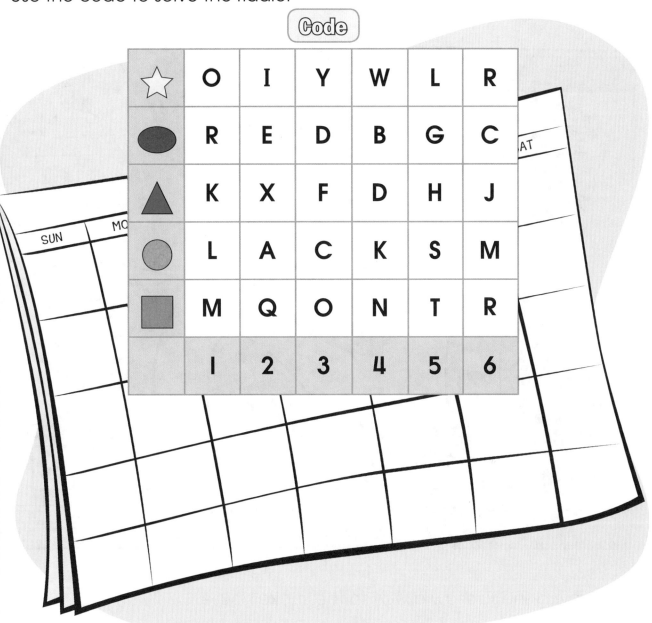

	1	2	3	4	5	6
☆	O	I	Y	W	L	R
⬤	R	E	D	B	G	C
▲	K	X	F	D	H	J
⬤	L	A	C	K	S	M
⬛	M	Q	O	N	T	R

Which month has 28 days?

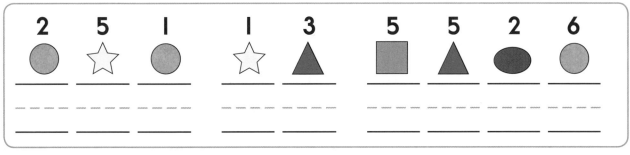

2	5	1	1	3	5	5	2	6
⬤	☆	⬤	☆	▲	⬛	▲	⬤	⬤

___ ___ ___   ___ ___   ___ ___ ___   ___

Look at the map and the map key.
Then follow the directions.

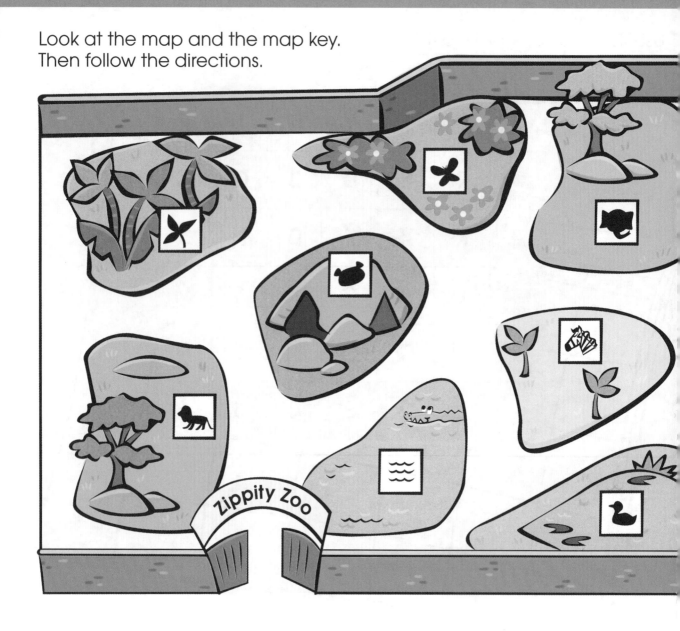

1. Draw a line to show a way to the snake house.

2. Draw a ☐ to show where you can see a tiger.

3. Draw a △ to show where you can see a duck.

4. Write the name of the place you would go first.

_____

- -

_____

Map Key

	Elephants		Bear Cave
	Rain Forest		Hooved Animals
	Snake House		Monkey Island
	Zebra Park		Butterfly Garden
	Water World		Big Cat Country
			Quackers Pond

Use the map to answer the questions.

5. Can you see an elephant in the zoo?   yes   no

6. Can you see a snake in the zoo?   yes   no

7. Can you see a snowman in the zoo?   yes   no

OFF TO THE DUDE RANCH

Ethan and Avery went to Circle S Ranch for the summer.
They need help getting from the entrance to the riding stables.
Use the map to answer the questions.

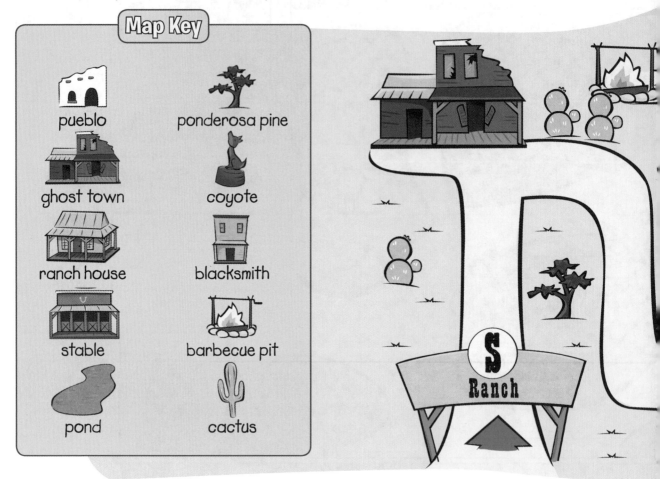

Map Key

pueblo

ponderosa pine

ghost town

coyote

ranch house

blacksmith

stable

barbecue pit

pond

cactus

1. What will they pass first?   ghost town   cows

2. Will they walk toward the blacksmith?   yes   no

3. Will they cross over a bridge?   yes   no

4. What will they pass after the bridge?   coyote   pueblo

5. What is the last thing they will pass?   barbecue pit   pond

6. Draw a line to show the path they followed.

7. Which two things would you like to see at Circle S Ranch?

_____

- -

_____

- -

_____

_____

_____

_____

_____

_____

Wendy and her mother are going shopping at the mall.
Use your pencil to follow their route.

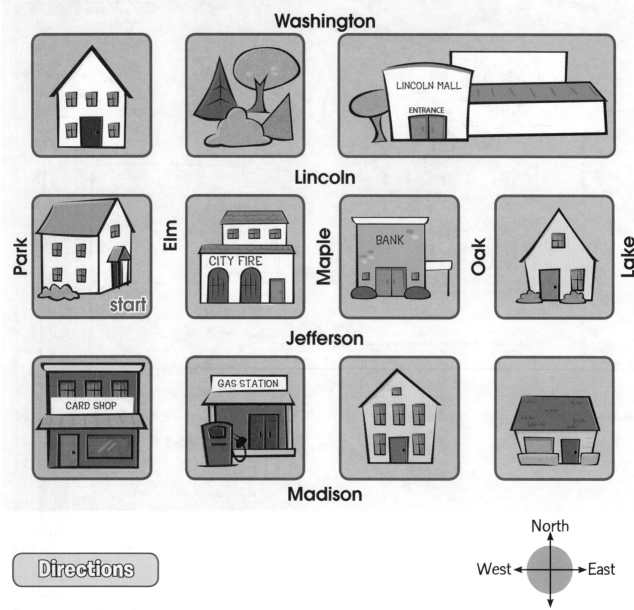

Directions

Begin on Elm Street. Walk to Jefferson Street.
Go west to Park Street. Turn north. Go to Washington Street.
Go east to Elm Street. Go south to Lincoln Street.
Go east and stop at the mall entrance.
Then, help them take the shortest route home.

North
Northwest   Northeast
West ◄——————► East
Southwest   Southeast
South

Use the map to answer the questions.
Circle the answers.

Cherry

Third Avenue

Hill

First Avenue   Second Avenue   Fourth Avenue   Fifth Avenue

Fountain

Third Avenue

Crescent

1. Which direction is Fifth Avenue from the school?

    North   South   East   West

2. Which direction is the zoo from the school?

    Northwest   Southeast   Northeast   Southwest

3. Which direction is the park from the school?

    Northeast   Southeast   Northwest   Southwest

4. Which direction is the post office from the school?

    Southwest   Northwest   Northeast   Southeast

NOUNS

A **noun** is a word that names a person, place, animal, or thing.

We are going to visit my <u>aunt</u>. (person)
She lives in a <u>forest</u>. (place)
She has a <u>puppy</u>. (animal)
She wrote a <u>book</u>. (thing)

One word in each sentence is a noun.
Read the sentences.
Write the nouns.

1. Billy wanted to go. _____

2. Dad drove away. _____

3. The farmer waved. _____

4. The cows were eating. _____

5. Our dog barked. _____

6. A chicken ran away. _____

NOUNS

Write the correct nouns that name animals to finish the sentences.

pig horse dog duck cow goat

1. The _____ is tall.

2. A _____ has a curly tail.

3. The _____ is eating.

4. A spotted _____ moos.

5. The _____ has a green head.

6. The _____ has a purple collar.

Which words name places? Which words name things?
Write the nouns in the correct columns.

zoo house pizza book town bike

places

_____

- - - - - - - - - - - - - - -

_____

- - - - - - - - - - - - - - -

_____

- - - - - - - - - - - - - - -

_____

things

_____

- - - - - - - - - - - - - - -

_____

- - - - - - - - - - - - - - -

_____

- - - - - - - - - - - - - - -

_____

Extra Credit!

Write a word that names a place and a word that names a thing.

place

_____

- - - - - - - - - - - - - - -

_____

thing

_____

- - - - - - - - - - - - - - -

_____

Remember! **Nouns** are words that name people, animals, places, or things. Draw a line through the nouns.

People

1

and	pat	red
dad	mom	brother
blue	the	sing

Animals

2

did	eat	cat
bake	rabbit	do
dog	come	sit

Places

3

sad	big	school
small	hot	zoo
happy	cold	beach

Things

4

ball	talk	jump
run	bike	tall
wide	sheep	car

NOUNS

Read the story.
Underline the nouns.

My family is busy working on the farm.
The cows are being milked.
Hens are laying eggs.
A neighbor is painting the fence.
The horse waits in the barn.
My uncle is out in the field on his tractor.
My brother is feeding the chickens.

Write the nouns from the story in the correct columns.

people

animals

places

things

Many nouns add **s** to name more than one.

one hen → two hen**s**
one frog → two frog**s**

---

dog spot ball bone ear name

Finish the sentences by writing the correct nouns from the box, adding **s** to make the nouns plural.

1. Jamie has two _____.

2. Their _____ are Mia and Jet.

3. One dog has brown ears and _____.

4. One dog has black _____.

5. They run after _____.

6. They bury _____.

Proper nouns name particular people, animals, places, and things. All proper nouns begin with uppercase letters.

Name: Ben
Place: Yellowstone National Park
Thing: The Empire State Building

A	P	E	T	E	R	H	J
F	D	A	X	Z	T	S	P
Q	V	V	G	H	P	L	O
B	U	B	B	L	E	S	L
H	F	X	Y	U	H	V	L
D	U	K	E	W	J	N	Y
Z	S	Q	V	T	D	U	Q
D	P	U	F	F	M	K	L

Find the names of the pets in the word search. Then answer the clues with proper nouns.

1. I can talk. _____

2. I chase mice. _____

3. I hop. _____

4. I live in water. _____

5. I bark at strangers. _____

PROPER NOUNS

The days of the week, months of the year, and holidays are proper nouns.

Monday   September   Christmas

Sunday	Monday	Tuesday	Wednesday	Thursday	Friday	Saturday
Sherman Sheep Shearing	Birthday Party for Coco the Camel	Storytime Safari with Keeper Katie	The Zoo Is for You Day! FREE DAY	Rain Forest Walk with Monte Monkey	Dusty Desert Trail Hike	Spring Egg Hunt

Write the days when these things happen.

1. _____

2. _____

3. _____

4. _____

VERBS

A **verb** is an action word that tells what someone or something does.

These words are verbs: run   jump   laugh   cry   eat   sleep

Read the sentences.
Write the verbs.

1. Let's play ball. _____

2. Jake hits the ball. _____

3. The ball flies high. _____

4. Wen runs after it. _____

5. Will she catch it? _____

6. Will Wen drop the ball? _____

VERBS

Roxanne wants to go to Suzie's house.
Help her get there by following the path of verbs.

Fun Fact
A verb doesn't always describe movement. For instance, **sleep, rest,** and **think** are verbs.

eat   run   dog   cat   big   rabbit

slide   bed

desk   jump   walk   small   sock

yarn   fly   bird

shell   house   dig   ball   shoes

city   hop

car   climb

cookie   wagon   hug   sing

Some verbs end with **s**.

dig**s**   sing**s**   jump**s**

---

plant eat water pull dig grow

Finish the sentences by writing the correct verbs from the box, adding **s** as needed.

_____

I. Each spring, Bob _____ a garden.

_____

2. He _____ pretty flowers.

_____

3. Dad _____ weeds.

_____

4. Anna _____ the garden.

_____

5. Sometimes, a rabbit _____ the flowers.

_____

6. Sometimes, a dog _____ in the garden.

Read the story.
Underline the verbs.

Five ducks waddle to the pond.
They jump into the cool water.
They paddle with their feet.
They dive under the water.
They bob back up.
They swim to the other side.
Then they fly away.

Circle the verbs that tell what the ducks did.

1.	How do the ducks get to the pond?	walk	waddle
2.	How do they get into the cool water?	jump	hop
3.	How do they get to the other side?	slide	swim
4.	How do they leave?	fly	jog

ADJECTIVES

An **adjective** is a describing word. It tells about a noun.
An adjective can be a number, size, or color.
An adjective can tell how something looks, sounds, or feels.
Many adjectives come before the nouns they describe.

There are little ladybugs in the garden. **Little** is an adjective.

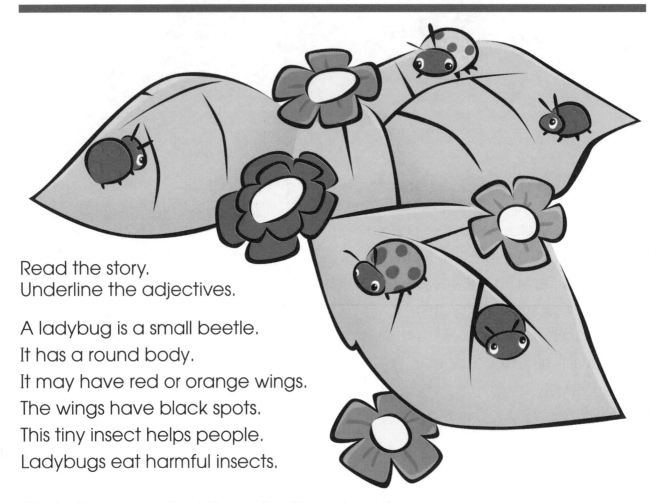

Read the story.
Underline the adjectives.

A ladybug is a small beetle.
It has a round body.
It may have red or orange wings.
The wings have black spots.
This tiny insect helps people.
Ladybugs eat harmful insects.

Circle the nouns that the adjectives describe.

I. "Small" describes   wings   beetle

2. "Red or orange" describes   wings   body

3. "Round" describes   body   spots

4. "Harmful" describes   wings   insects

ADJECTIVES

Write the correct adjectives to finish the sentences.

hot cold loud wet quiet soft

_____

1. The sun is _____.

_____

2. A jet makes a _____ sound.

_____

3. Ice cream is _____.

_____

4. The kitten has _____ fur.

_____

5. Don't slip on the _____ grass.

_____

6. The _____ deer hides.

Write the correct adjectives to finish the sentences.

1. I like to read on _____ days.

2. Kites fly high when it is _____.

3. Days the sun is hidden are _____.

4. We need to wear boots when it is _____.

ADJECTIVES

Read the sentences.
Underline the adjectives.
Draw lines from the sentences to the cats they describe.

1. Lady is a big cat.

2. She had three kittens.

3. Tiger is the striped kitten.

4. Jet is the black kitten.

5. The little kitten is Socks.

6. We now have four cats.

The **subject** of a sentence tells who or what the sentence is about.

<u>My family</u> went on a trip.
"My family" tells who this sentence is about.

<u>The trip</u> took six hours.
"The trip" tells what this sentence is about.

Read the sentences.
Underline the subjects.
Then circle who or what.

1. Our family visited Yellowstone National Park.   who   what

2. The park has lakes and springs.   who   what

3. People camp in the park.   who   what

4. Stars fill the night sky.   who   what

5. Forests are everywhere.   who   what

6. Hikers climb hills.   who   what

Write subjects to finish the sentences.

7. _____ is fun to visit.

8. _____ and I go there a lot.

In addition to a subject, a sentence also has a **predicate**.
The predicate includes a verb and tells what the subject is or does.

The friends <u>made plans for a picnic</u>.
"Made plans for a picnic" tells what "the friends" did.

Read the sentences.
Underline the predicates.

1. Dani brings milk.

2. Josh grabs bananas.

3. Kim takes a salad.

4. Billy carries hot dogs.

5. They all eat together.

Extra Credit!

Write a sentence that tells what you would bring to a picnic.
Underline the predicate.

_____

_____

_____

_____

PREDICATES

Read the sentences.
Underline the predicates.

1. Owls hunt at night.

2. Elk eat green plants.

3. Eagles nest in the park.

4. Water shoots up from underground.

5. Hikers walk down trails.

6. The forest is quiet.

Write predicates to finish the sentences.

7. Campers _____.

8. A squirrel _____.

USE CLUES!

Sometimes the **context**, or surrounding word clues, will help you understand a word you don't know. Practice using context clues to determine which word is missing.

The cheese was (moldy/tasty), so I threw it in the garbage.
You would throw moldy cheese in the garbage.

Circle the words that belong.
Underline the clues that helped you decide.

1. I love fruit, so I packed a (banana/pizza) for lunch.

2. A feather tickled my nose, so I (sneezed/cried).

3. The snow was (pretty/heavy). It broke the tree limb.

4. It was my birthday, so we had a (circus/party).

5. He gave his mom a rose. She (smiled/frowned) and said, "Thank you."

WHO, WHERE, WHEN, AND WHY?

Write the correct words to answer the riddles.

> **when   why   who   where**

1. I am the word that asks for a <u>name</u>.

   _____

   _____

2. I am the word that asks for a <u>place</u>.

   _____

   _____

3. I am the word that asks for a <u>time</u>.

   _____

   _____

4. I am the word that asks for a <u>reason</u>.

   _____

   _____

You're Invited to a
Birthday Party
for Matthew!

Scott
Name

May 20
Date

_7 PM_
Time

Matthew's House
Place

Extra Credit!

Write a sentence that tells the month of your birthday.

_____

_____

_____

_____

STATEMENTS

A **statement** is a sentence that tells something.
A statement begins with an uppercase letter and ends with a **period** (.).

Our dog's name is Skip.

When writers are editing their work, this symbol ☰ goes under the letter
that needs to be an uppercase letter.
Use ☰ to show where uppercase letters go.
Put periods (.) at the end of the sentences.
The first one is done for you.

1. <u>o</u>ur dog is hungry.

2. dad brings food

3. skip eats quickly

4. food goes on the floor

5. dogs are messy

6. now I need to clean up

Extra Credit!

Write a statement that tells something about your favorite animal.

_____

- -

_____

- -

_____

A **question** is a sentence that asks about someone or something. A question begins with an uppercase letter and ends with a **question mark** (?).

What is your favorite color?

Use ≡ to show where uppercase letters go.
Put question marks at the end of the sentences that ask questions.
Put a period at the end of the statement.
The first one is done for you.

1. i̲s̲ mother home?

2. where did she go

3. when will she be back

4. who baked the cookies

5. they are good

6. may i have another one

(**Extra Credit!**)

Write a question about your favorite food.

_____

- - - - - - - - - - - - - - - - - - -

_____

_____

- - - - - - - - - - - - - - - - - - -

_____

EXCLAMATIONS

An **exclamation** is a sentence that shows strong feeling. An exclamation begins with an uppercase letter and ends with an **exclamation point** (!).

I can't believe we won!
We're the best!

Write exclamation points at the end of the exclamations.
Write periods at the end of the statements.

1. My team played soccer today

2. The most amazing thing happened

3. The score was 3 to 3

4. Our team got the ball

5. We made a goal

6. It was awesome

Extra Credit!

Write an exclamation about your favorite sport.

_____

- -

_____

_____

- -

_____

The snowman is melting.

Why did this happen?

The sun came out and the temperature rose.

The sun and the rising temperature **caused** the snowman to melt.
The **effect** of the sun and the rising temperature is the melting snowman.

Read the effect. Write the cause.

1. The dog is eating.

Why did this happen?

_____

_____

_____

Read the effects. Write the causes.

1. The sidewalk has dog prints in it.

Why did this happen?

_____

- -

_____

_____

2. A dog has a ball in his mouth.

Why did this happen?

_____

- -

_____

_____

Read the effects. Write the causes.

1. Jason has a tomato from the garden.

Why did this happen?

_____

_____

_____

2. The bird feeder is filling up with birdseed.

Why did this happen?

_____

_____

_____

CAUSE AND EFFECT RELATIONSHIPS

Put a check mark by what you think will happen next.

1. The baby is hungry.

   _____ The baby is given a toy.

   _____ The baby is given dinner.

2. The family dog is lost.

   _____ The family looks for it.

   _____ The family watches TV.

3. It begins to rain at the picnic.

   _____ The family eats.

   _____ The family packs up and leaves.

4. The car has a flat tire.

   _____ The tire is fixed.

   _____ The car is sold.

5. Bill's shirt is torn.

   _____ Bill wears the torn shirt.

   _____ Bill puts on a new shirt.

Circle the pictures that show what happened next.

1. Mick loves movies. He goes to a movie whenever he has money. Mick got $10.00 from his uncle. What happened next?

2. Morgan's mom gave her flower seeds. Morgan made a garden. She planted the seeds every which way. What happened next?

3. Mia's pup chewed her homework. He chewed a chair leg. Mia left her shoes in the yard. What happened next?

CAUSE AND EFFECT RELATIONSHIPS

Circle the pictures that show what happened next.

1. Jack turned on the water. He was going to wash the dishes. Jack started talking to his friend. What happened next?

2. Kathy's mom went out. Kathy cleaned the house. Her mom came home. What happened next?

3. Eva went to the library. She picked out a book. She couldn't wait to read it. Eva took the book home. What happened next?

Draw a line from the cause to its effect.

Cause	**Effect**

Write about the cause and effects.

1. What would happen if you dropped a glass?

_____

_____

2. What would happen if you touched something hot?

_____

_____

3. What would cause you to laugh?

_____

_____

Read the story.

This is my cat.
His name is Pat.
Pat sat on his mat.
Oh! Pat saw a bat.
Pat ran after the bat.
Drat!
Pat could not catch the bat.
Pat sat back on his mat.

Number the sentences from
1 to 4 to show the correct order.

_____

_____ Pat ran after the bat.

_____

_____ Pat could not catch the bat.

_____

_____ Pat sat back on his mat.

_____

_____ Pat saw a bat.

SID THE SNAKE

Read the story.

Sid the Snake makes shapes.
Sid can make a circle.
Sid can make an s.
Sid cannot make a triangle.
Sid cannot make a square.

Circle the correct answers.

1. What is the best name for the story?

   Real Snake   Sid's Shapes

2. What shape can Sid make?

   circle   square

3. Can Sid make a triangle?

   yes   no

4. Can Sid make an s?

   yes   no

5. Draw a square.

6. Draw a triangle.

THE MYSTERY BUS

Read the story.

Amy got on the bus.
It was her first bus ride ever.
Amy sat next to her friend Sue.
The bus stopped many times.
Other kids got on the bus.

Circle the correct answers.

1. What did Amy get on?   bus   boat

2. Who did Amy sit next to?   Jon   Sue

3. Who else got on the bus?   dogs   kids

4. Had Amy been on a bus ride before?   yes   no

5. Did the bus stop often?   yes   no

6. Where was the bus going?   school   home
   _____

7. How many stops did the bus make? _____

BEN'S PET HEN

Read the story.

Ben has a pet hen.
The hen is red.
The hen lives in a pen.
The red hen lays eggs for Ben.
She lays one egg a day.
How many days until Ben has ten?
_____

- -

_____

Put a check mark by the correct answer.

1. Which is the best title for the story?

_____ Ben's Hen

_____ Ben Likes Breakfast

_____ The Hen's Pen

2. Which sentence tells what the story is about?

_____ The hen lays eggs.

_____ Ben has a pet hen.

_____ The hen lives in a pen.

ANNA'S RACE

Read the story.

Anna was in a bike race.
There were five riders in the race.
They lined up to begin.
Anna got a surprise.
Her bike had a flat tire!
Anna did not mind.
She will try another time.

1. Put a check mark by what the story is about.

   _____ Anna was in a bike race.

   _____ Her bike had a flat tire.

   _____ Anna did not mind.

   _____ Anna got a surprise.

2. How many riders were in the race? _____

Extra Credit!

Write a sentence about a time when you were riding a bike.

_____
_____
_____
_____

THE FOX ON THE ROCK

Read the story.

Scott was on the dock.
He had a fishing rod.
Scott saw something on the rock.
It was a fox.
The fox saw Scott.
It ran from the rock.
That is the last Scott saw of the fox.

Write T if the sentence is true.
Write F if the sentence is false.

1. _____ The fox was on the dock.

2. _____ Scott saw a fox.

3. _____ The fox ran from the rock.

4. _____ The fox had a fishing rod.

Extra Credit!

Write a sentence about what you would do if you saw a fox.

_____

_____

_____

A RACE IN THE RAIN

Read the story.

It was Play Day for the garden animals.
The turtle and snail decided to race.
First, they had to find a safe place.
They found a trail near the gate.
Wait! It is beginning to rain.
Waves of water washed out the trail.
The race never took place.

Answer the questions.

1. Who do you think would have won the race?

   _____

   _____

2. Which is the best title for the story?
   Put a check mark by your answer.

   _____ The Trail   _____ Play Day

   _____ Near the Gate   _____ Waves of Water

Extra Credit!

Write about animals you would like to see race. Be sure to tell the
reader why you would like to see the animals race.

_____

_____

_____

_____

Read the story.

Eric was walking to school.
There were puddles by the road.
A car went past.
Eric looked surprised.

Circle the correct answers.

1. What was Eric doing?

   walking to school

   walking to the park

2. Why did Eric look surprised?

   He did not know the driver.

   The car splashed water on him.

Extra Credit!

What do you think Eric will do next?

_____
- -
_____
_____
- -
_____
_____
- -
_____

LOST AND FOUND

Read the story.

Jill went shopping for shoes.
She lost her purse.
Later, a call came from the lost-and-found desk.
Jill looked happy after the call.

Circle the correct answers.

1. What was Jill doing?

   shopping for shoes

   shopping for groceries

2. What did Jill lose?

   her hat

   her purse

3. Why do you think Jill looked happy?

   Her purse had been found.

   The store had the shoes she wanted.

Extra Credit!

What do you think Jill will do next?

_____

_____

_____

Read the note.

Dear Jeremy,
We're having a party on the 4th of July. We can watch fireworks! Will you come? There will be a picnic at 6:00. Bring food you like to eat.
See you there,
Tyrone

Answer the questions.

1. What kind of writing is this?

   an invitation   a song   a book

2. What kind of party is it?

3. What time is the party?

4. What should Jeremy bring?

5. What will they do at the party?

Read the sign.

Welcome to the Park!
The park is open from 9:00 to 5:00.
Come see the show!
Shows are at 10:00 and 2:00.
Rules:
Do not feed the animals.
Do not litter.
Do not pick the wildflowers.
DO HAVE FUN!

Circle the correct answers.

1. What kind of writing is this?

   a sign   a song   a book

2. Where would you find this?

   at school   in the park   in church

3. When do the shows start?

   10:00 and 9:00   9:00 and 5:00   10:00 and 2:00

Extra Credit!

Why do you think the sign tells people not to feed the animals?

_____

_____

_____

_____

Read the story.

Sshh... You are in a library.
People read in the library.
Please be quiet.

You can pick out a book at the library.
You can take the book home to read it.
Remember to bring the book back!

Circle the correct answers.

1. What is the story about?

    people   real things

    the library   storybooks

2. What can you do at the library?

    pick out a book   watch a show

    eat lunch   make noise

3. What should you remember to do with your book?

    be quiet   bring it back   give it away

Extra Credit!

Write a sentence about your favorite book.

_____

_____

_____

_____

_____

_____

BOOK COVERS

Read about book covers.

Books covers tell about books.
The words on the cover tell the
title of the book.
They tell who wrote the book.

Circle the correct answers.

1. Which things do book covers tell us?

   who wrote the book   the title of the book

   when the book was made

Read the book cover.
Then answer the questions.

2. Who wrote this book?

   _____

   _____

3. What is the title of this book?

   _____

   _____

4. What do you think this book is about?

   _____

   _____

Read the story about bugs.

I do not think bugs are fun!
What can you do with a bug?
Can you give a bug a hug?
I go mad with their buzz, buzz, buzz.
When I see a bug, I want to run.
I do not think bugs are fun!

We sometimes call insects "bugs."

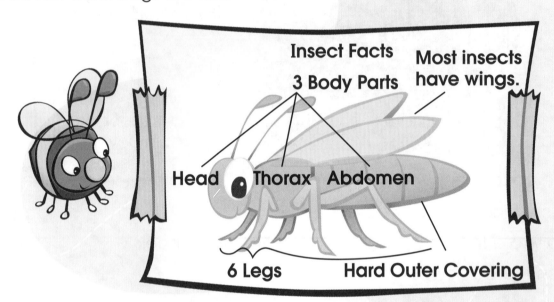

Insect Facts

3 Body Parts

Most insects have wings.

Head   Thorax   Abdomen

6 Legs   Hard Outer Covering

Write T if the sentence is true.
Write F if the sentence is false.

1. _____ Insects have six legs.

2. _____ Most insects have wings.

3. _____ An insect's body has three parts.

4. _____ Insects do not have a hard outer covering.

SLOW SNAILS

Read about snails.

A snail has a soft body covered by a shell.
It creeps along on a foot.
A snail makes a sticky slime to help it move.
Many land snails eat rotting plants.
They lay eggs in the ground.
Land snails live in shady places.

Answer the questions.

1. How do snails move?
   _____
   _____
   _____

2. Where do land snails live?
   _____
   _____
   _____

3. What do many land snails eat?
   _____
   _____
   _____

4. Where do snails lay their eggs?
   _____
   _____
   _____

Read the note.

> Mom,
> I'm outside. I went to
> the park. Adam is with me.
> We will be home by noon.
> 					I love you,
> 					Erica

1. Write a sentence that tells who wrote the note.

_____

_____

2. Write a sentence that tells who is with Erica.

_____

_____

3. Write a sentence that tells where they are going.

_____

_____

4. Write a sentence that tells when they will be home.

_____

_____

JUMPING CHANT

Read the poem.

Flowers in the garden.
Flowers by the walk.
Flowers in the forest.
I wish that they could talk.

Flowers dancing in the wind
And sprouting up in May.
If I met a flower friend,
What would it have to say?

Circle the correct answers.

1. What kind of writing is this?
   a letter   a story   a poem

2. What do flowers do in the wind?
   grow   dance   talk

3. What does "sprouting up" mean?
   getting planted   starting to grow

Draw a line between the words that rhyme.

4. walk   shower

5. May   talk

6. flower   say

7. wish   fish

A **setting** is where a story takes place.
Read the two stories. Answer the questions.

Harry went to see the animals at the zoo.
There were animals that came from places around the world.
He knew he would not see these animals where he lived.

1. Where did Harry see the animals?

   zoo   farm

   city   school

2. What animals do you think Harry saw at the zoo?

   _____
   -
   _____
   _____
   -
   _____

3. Write a sentence about your favorite animal at the zoo.

   _____
   -
   _____
   _____
   -
   _____

Jill does not want to be late.

She must hurry before the bell rings.

She looks down the hall and sees only one door still open.

4. Where does this story take place?

   at home   at school

   at the zoo   at the store

5. What do you think Jill will do next?

   _____

   _____

   _____

   _____

   _____

6. What do you think is behind the open door?

   Jill's bedroom   a farm

   a classroom   a beach

7. Write a sentence about a time you had to hurry!

   _____

   _____

   _____

   _____

   _____

Read the story.

Summer is my favorite time of the year.
I can go to the beach. I can play games in my yard.
I can wear shorts and t-shirts. I can wear flip-flops.
Winter is cold. I must wear a heavy coat, a hat, and mittens.
I often have to wear boots because it has snowed.
Many winter days are without sunshine.
But, I can still play with my friends whether it's summer or winter.

coat shorts friends hat boots t-shirts flip-flops beach

Write the words from the box where they belong in the diagram.

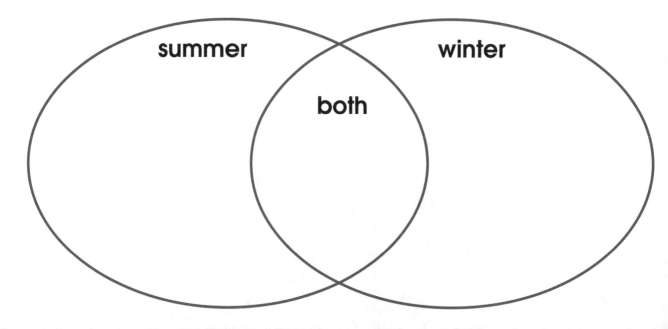

summer   winter

both

The answer to an addition problem is called the **sum**.
You can write an **addition number sentence** like this: **2 + 3 = 5.**

$$\underline{2} + \underline{3} = \underline{5}$$

Write addition number sentences about the pictures.

1. _____ + _____ = _____

2. _____ + _____ = _____

3. _____ + _____ = _____

4. _____ + _____ = _____

5. _____ + _____ = _____

6. _____ + _____ = _____

7. _____ + _____ = _____

$$\underline{\;5\;} + \underline{\;2\;} = \underline{\;7\;}$$

Write addition number sentences about the pictures.

1. _____ + _____ = _____

2. _____ + _____ = _____

3. _____ + _____ = _____

4. _____ + _____ = _____

5. _____ + _____ = _____

6. _____ + _____ = _____

7. _____ + _____ = _____

+

$\underline{\quad 5 \quad} + \underline{\quad 6 \quad} = \underline{\quad 11 \quad}$

Write the **sums**.

1. $8 + 3 = $ _____

2. $5 + 7 = $ _____

3. $6 + 4 = $ _____

4. $9 + 2 = $ _____

5. $1 + 8 = $ _____

6. $7 + 2 = $ _____

7. $5 + 6 = $ _____

8. $9 + 0 = $ _____

9. $5 + 5 = $ _____

10. $\begin{array}{r} 9 \\ +3 \\ \hline \end{array}$

11. $\begin{array}{r} 2 \\ +8 \\ \hline \end{array}$

12. $\begin{array}{r} 7 \\ +4 \\ \hline \end{array}$

13. $\begin{array}{r} 6 \\ +6 \\ \hline \end{array}$

14. $\begin{array}{r} 8 \\ +4 \\ \hline \end{array}$

15. $\begin{array}{r} 9 \\ +1 \\ \hline \end{array}$

16. $\begin{array}{r} 4 \\ +5 \\ \hline \end{array}$

17. $\begin{array}{r} 7 \\ +3 \\ \hline \end{array}$

18. $\begin{array}{r} 8 \\ +2 \\ \hline \end{array}$

19. $\begin{array}{r} 7 \\ +5 \\ \hline \end{array}$

20. $\begin{array}{r} 6 \\ +3 \\ \hline \end{array}$

21. $\begin{array}{r} 4 \\ +7 \\ \hline \end{array}$

THREE ADDENDS

The numbers you add are called **addends**.
You can add three numbers in different ways.

Add the numbers in order:
Add the first two numbers.
$4 + 2 = 6$

$$\begin{array}{r} 4 \\ 2 \\ + 6 \\ \hline 12 \end{array}$$

$4 \; \rceil = 6$
$2 \; \rfloor$

Then add the third number.
$6 + 6 = 12$

Look for a ten:
Look for two numbers with the sum of 10.
$4 + 6 = 10$

$$\begin{array}{r} 4 \\ 2 \\ + 6 \\ \hline 12 \end{array} = 10$$

Then add the third number.
$10 + 2 = 12$

Write the **sums**.

1.
$$\begin{array}{r} 2 \\ 6 \\ + 3 \\ \hline \end{array}$$

2.
$$\begin{array}{r} 1 \\ 8 \\ + 3 \\ \hline \end{array}$$

3.
$$\begin{array}{r} 9 \\ 1 \\ + 2 \\ \hline \end{array}$$

4.
$$\begin{array}{r} 2 \\ 4 \\ + 5 \\ \hline \end{array}$$

5.
$$\begin{array}{r} 4 \\ 7 \\ + 1 \\ \hline \end{array}$$

6.
$$\begin{array}{r} 4 \\ 4 \\ + 2 \\ \hline \end{array}$$

7.
$$\begin{array}{r} 3 \\ 1 \\ + 7 \\ \hline \end{array}$$

8.
$$\begin{array}{r} 5 \\ 5 \\ + 2 \\ \hline \end{array}$$

9.
$$\begin{array}{r} 6 \\ 2 \\ + 2 \\ \hline \end{array}$$

10.
$$\begin{array}{r} 4 \\ 4 \\ + 4 \\ \hline \end{array}$$

11.
$$\begin{array}{r} 3 \\ 2 \\ + 5 \\ \hline \end{array}$$

12.
$$\begin{array}{r} 1 \\ 2 \\ + 8 \\ \hline \end{array}$$

How many are there in each group?
Draw a line from the group to the number.
The first one is done for you.

1

2

3

4

5

6

7

8

9

10

DRAWING OBJECTS FOR NUMBERS

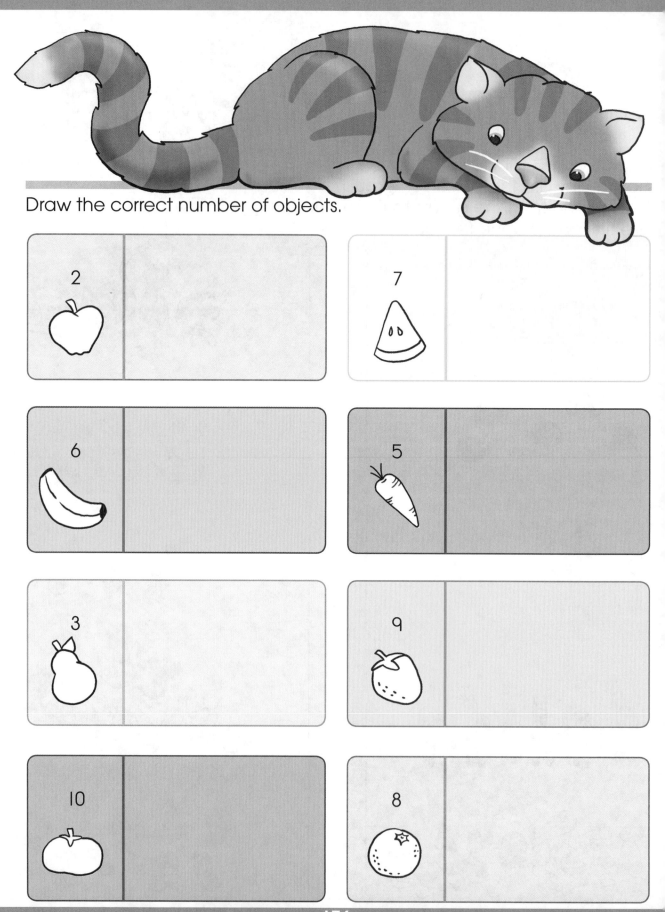

Draw the correct number of objects.

2

7

6

5

3

9

10

8

ANIMAL FRIENDS

> HINT! When you see these words, you should add: **in all**, **altogether**, **total**, and **sum**.

Amy has **3** cats.
Dan has **2** cats.
What is the **total** number of cats?

__3__ + __2__ = __5__ cats

Read and solve each word problem.

1. Jason saw **2** birds.
   Then he saw **6** more birds.
   How many birds did he see **in all**?

_____ + _____ = _____ birds

---

2. Katy has **1** turtle.
   Marco has **5** turtles.
   How many turtles do they have **altogether**?

_____ + _____ = _____ turtles

---

3. Pedro has **4** dogs.
   Gary has **3** dogs.
   What is the **total** number of dogs?

_____ + _____ = _____ dogs

Write how many animals there are.

1.

_____

2.

_____

3.

_____

4.

_____

5.

_____

6.

_____

7.

_____

8.

_____

More means a bigger number.

← This group has **more** penguins.

Circle the group that has **more** animals.

7. Draw a group of 🐟 to show **I more** than **3**.

How many 🐟 are there? _____

Greater means **more than**.
5 is **greater** than **3**.

⑤ birds   **3** birds

Write how many there are in each group. Circle the number that is **greater**.

1.

_____   _____

2.

_____   _____

3.

_____   _____

4.

_____   _____

5.

_____   _____

6.

_____   _____

Fewer means a smaller number.

← This group has **fewer** bats.

Circle the group that has **fewer** animals.

1.

2.

3.

4.

5.

6.

7. Draw a group of 🦋 to show **1 fewer** than **10**.

How many 🦋 are there? _____

WHICH NUMBER IS LESS?

Less means **fewer** or not as many.
9 is **less** than **10**.

⑨ bees   **10** bees

Write how many there are in each group. Circle the number that is **less**.

1.

_____   _____

2.

_____   _____

3.

_____   _____

4.

_____   _____

5.

_____   _____

6.

_____   _____

The answer to an addition problem is called the **sum**.

3 is the **sum** in this addition number sentence: **1 + 2 = 3**

Look at the picture. Read the number sentence. Write the **sum**.

1.

1 + 1 = _____

2.

1 + 2 = _____

3.

1 + 3 = _____

4.

1 + 4 = _____

5.

2 + 1 = _____

6.

2 + 2 = _____

7.

2 + 3 = _____

8.

4 + 1 = _____

MORE ADDING

$$
\begin{array}{r}
1 \\
+ \ 2 \\
\hline
3
\end{array}
$$
← sum

Look at the picture. Read the problem. Write the **sum**.

1.

$$
\begin{array}{r}
2 \\
+ \ 1 \\
\hline
\end{array}
$$

2.

$$
\begin{array}{r}
1 \\
+ \ 4 \\
\hline
\end{array}
$$

3.

$$
\begin{array}{r}
3 \\
+ \ 2 \\
\hline
\end{array}
$$

4.

$$
\begin{array}{r}
1 \\
+ \ 3 \\
\hline
\end{array}
$$

5.

$$
\begin{array}{r}
2 \\
+ \ 3 \\
\hline
\end{array}
$$

6.

$$
\begin{array}{r}
1 \\
+ \ 1 \\
\hline
\end{array}
$$

7.

$$
\begin{array}{r}
2 \\
+ \ 2 \\
\hline
\end{array}
$$

8.

$$
\begin{array}{r}
4 \\
+ \ 1 \\
\hline
\end{array}
$$

SUBTRACTING TO FIND THE DIFFERENCE

The answer to a subtraction problem is called the **difference**.

5 - 2 = ____3____

3 is the **difference** in this subtraction number sentence: **5 - 2 = 3**

Look at the picture. Read the number sentence. Write the **difference**.

1.

3 - 1 = _____

2.

4 - 1 = _____

3.

4 - 2 = _____

4.

5 - 4 = _____

5.

4 - 3 = _____

6.

5 - 3 = _____

7.

3 - 2 = _____

8.

2 - 1 = _____

Remember! The answer to a subtraction problem is called the **difference**. You can write a **subtraction number sentence** like this: **4 – 2 = 2**.

$$\underline{}4\ -\ \underline{}2\ =\ \underline{}2$$

Write number sentences about the pictures.

1. _____ – _____ = _____

2. _____ – _____ = _____

3. _____ – _____ = _____

4. _____ – _____ = _____

5. _____ – _____ = _____

6. _____ – _____ = _____

7. _____ – _____ = _____

$$\underline{7} - \underline{3} = \underline{4}$$

Write number sentences about the pictures.

1.

_____ - _____ = _____

2.

_____ - _____ = _____

3.

_____ - _____ = _____

4.

_____ - _____ = _____

5.

_____ - _____ = _____

6.

_____ - _____ = _____

7.

_____ - _____ = _____

$$\underline{10} - \underline{6} = \underline{4}$$

Write number sentences about the pictures.

1.

_____ – _____ = _____

2.

_____ – _____ = _____

3.

_____ – _____ = _____

4.

_____ – _____ = _____

5.

_____ – _____ = _____

6.

_____ – _____ = _____

7.

_____ – _____ = _____

Write the **differences**. An example is done for you.

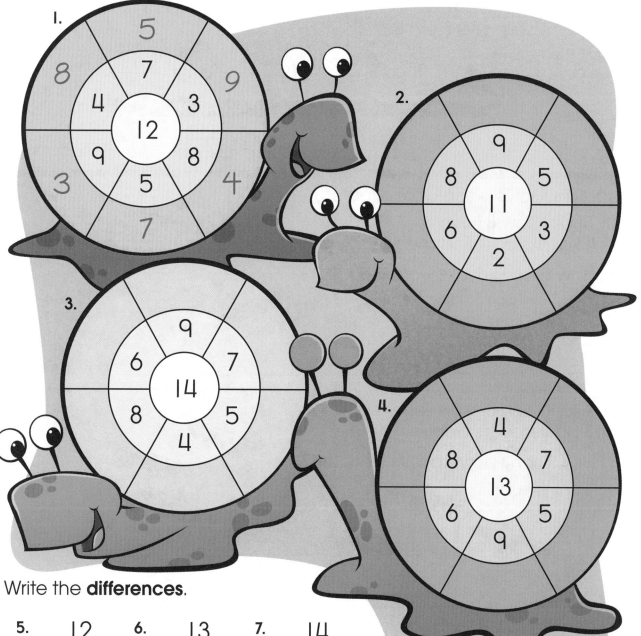

Write the **differences**.

5. 12
    − 9

6. 13
    − 8

7. 14
    − 8

8. 11
    − 9

9. 12
    − 8

10. 14
    − 7

Connor saw **7** sailboats.
2 sailboats sailed away.

How many sailboats were **left**?

_7_ – _2_ = _5_ sailboats

Read and solve each word problem.

1. Tiffany saw **8** kayaks.
   4 kayaks paddled away.

   How many kayaks were **left**?

   _____ – _____ = _____ kayaks

2. Allison saw **6** powerboats.
   3 powerboats went away.

   How many powerboats were **left**?

   _____ – _____ = _____ powerboats

3. Jordan saw **8** surfboards.
   2 surfboards floated away.

   How many surfboards were **left**?

   _____ – _____ = _____ surfboards

There are **6** frogs.
There are **4** lily pads.

How many **more** frogs are there than lily pads?

_6_ – _4_ = _2_ frogs

Read and solve each word problem.

1. There are **5** fish.
   There are **4** cattails.

   How many **more** fish are there than cattails?

_____ – _____ = _____ fish

---

2. There are **8** flowers.
   There are **4** butterflies.

   How many **more** flowers are there than butterflies?

_____ – _____ = _____ flowers

---

3. There are **7** turtles.
   There are **5** logs.

   How many **more** turtles are there than logs?

_____ – _____ = _____ turtles

$$\begin{array}{r} 3 \\ -\ 1 \\ \hline 2 \end{array}$$ ← **difference**

Look at the picture. Read the problem. Write the **difference**.

1.

$$\begin{array}{r} 5 \\ -\ 1 \\ \hline \end{array}$$

2.

$$\begin{array}{r} 5 \\ -\ 2 \\ \hline \end{array}$$

3.

$$\begin{array}{r} 5 \\ -\ 3 \\ \hline \end{array}$$

4.

$$\begin{array}{r} 3 \\ -\ 1 \\ \hline \end{array}$$

5.

$$\begin{array}{r} 4 \\ -\ 2 \\ \hline \end{array}$$

6.

$$\begin{array}{r} 3 \\ -\ 2 \\ \hline \end{array}$$

7.

$$\begin{array}{r} 2 \\ -\ 1 \\ \hline \end{array}$$

8.

$$\begin{array}{r} 4 \\ -\ 1 \\ \hline \end{array}$$

Fill in the addition facts table by finding the **sums**.
Color your answers. Do you see a pattern?

+	0	1	2	3	4	5
0	0					
1						
2				5		
3		4				
4						
5						

2 + 3 = 5

0 = Red

1 = Purple

2 = Blue

3 = Orange

4 = Yellow

5 = Green

Watch the signs!

If you are adding, write the **sum**. If you are subtracting, write the **difference**. The addition facts table on page 193 may help you.

1. $3 + 1 =$ _____

2. $3 - 1 =$ _____

3. $2 + 0 =$ _____

4. $5 - 1 =$ _____

5. $2 + 3 =$ _____

6. $4 - 3 =$ _____

7. $2 - 0 =$ _____

8. $1 + 2 =$ _____

9. $4 + 1 =$ _____

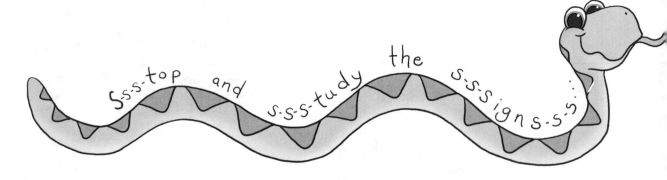

S-s-s-top and s-s-s-tudy the s-s-signs-s-s!

10.
$$\begin{array}{r} 3 \\ + 1 \\ \hline \end{array}$$

11.
$$\begin{array}{r} 2 \\ - 1 \\ \hline \end{array}$$

12.
$$\begin{array}{r} 5 \\ + 0 \\ \hline \end{array}$$

13.
$$\begin{array}{r} 4 \\ - 1 \\ \hline \end{array}$$

14.
$$\begin{array}{r} 3 \\ - 2 \\ \hline \end{array}$$

15.
$$\begin{array}{r} 0 \\ + 3 \\ \hline \end{array}$$

16.
$$\begin{array}{r} 2 \\ + 2 \\ \hline \end{array}$$

17.
$$\begin{array}{r} 3 \\ - 0 \\ \hline \end{array}$$

6 + 3 = __9__

You may count all the fish to find how many there are in all.

Look at the picture. Read the addition number sentence. Write the **sum**.

1.

4 + 3 = _____

2.

2 + 6 = _____

3.

4 + 3 =

2 + 7 = _____

4.

4 + 2 = _____

5.

5 + 5 = _____

6.

1 + 6 = _____

7.

6 + 4 = _____

8.

4 + 5 = _____

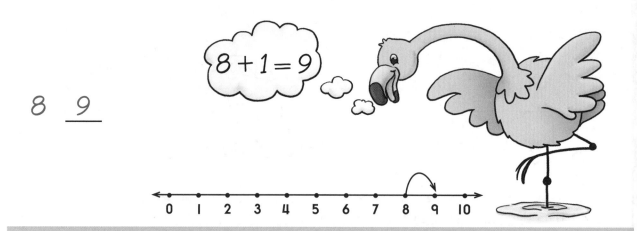

$8 + 1 = 9$

8 9

0 1 2 3 4 5 6 7 8 9 10

1. Add **1** to each number.
Write the **sum**.

6 _____
8 _____
7 _____
9 _____

2. Add **2** to each number.
Write the **sum**.

5 _____
7 _____
8 _____
6 _____

The way to an A

3. Add **3** to each number.
Write the **sum**.

5 _____
6 _____
4 _____
7 _____

4. Add **4** to each number.
Write the **sum**.

5 _____
3 _____
4 _____
6 _____

Fill in the addition facts table by writing the **sums**.

+	0	1	2	3	4	5	6	7	8	9
0	0						6			
1										
2						7				
3								10		
4										
5										
6										
7		8								
8										
9										

Write the **sums**.

$9 + 1 = $ _____

$8 + 2 = $ _____

$7 + 3 = $ _____

$6 + 4 = $ _____

$5 + 5 = $ _____

ADDITION FACT PAIRS

Look at the addition facts table on page 197.
Find these facts in the table. What do you notice?

When you know one fact, you can think of another fact.

$3 + 5 = \underline{8}$ $7 + 0 = \underline{7}$

$5 + 3 = \underline{8}$ $0 + 7 = \underline{7}$

Write the **sums**. The addition facts table on page 197 may help you.

1. $6 + 3 = \underline{\hspace{1cm}}$ 2. $5 + 2 = \underline{\hspace{1cm}}$ 3. $7 + 3 = \underline{\hspace{1cm}}$

   $3 + 6 = \underline{\hspace{1cm}}$ $2 + 5 = \underline{\hspace{1cm}}$ $3 + 7 = \underline{\hspace{1cm}}$

4. $9 + 1 = \underline{\hspace{1cm}}$ 5. $6 + 2 = \underline{\hspace{1cm}}$ 6. $8 + 0 = \underline{\hspace{1cm}}$

   $1 + 9 = \underline{\hspace{1cm}}$ $2 + 6 = \underline{\hspace{1cm}}$ $0 + 8 = \underline{\hspace{1cm}}$

Write the **sum** and another addition fact that uses the same numbers.

7. $4 + 5 = \underline{\hspace{1cm}}$ 8. $3 + 4 = \underline{\hspace{1cm}}$ 9. $6 + 0 = \underline{\hspace{1cm}}$

   $\underline{\hspace{0.7cm}} + \underline{\hspace{0.7cm}} = \underline{\hspace{0.7cm}}$ $\underline{\hspace{0.7cm}} + \underline{\hspace{0.7cm}} = \underline{\hspace{0.7cm}}$ $\underline{\hspace{0.7cm}} + \underline{\hspace{0.7cm}} = \underline{\hspace{0.7cm}}$

10. $8 + 2 = \underline{\hspace{1cm}}$ 11. $0 + 9 = \underline{\hspace{1cm}}$ 12. $1 + 7 = \underline{\hspace{1cm}}$

   $\underline{\hspace{0.7cm}} + \underline{\hspace{0.7cm}} = \underline{\hspace{0.7cm}}$ $\underline{\hspace{0.7cm}} + \underline{\hspace{0.7cm}} = \underline{\hspace{0.7cm}}$ $\underline{\hspace{0.7cm}} + \underline{\hspace{0.7cm}} = \underline{\hspace{0.7cm}}$

Use each group of numbers to write addition facts.

13. $2, 7, 9$ 14. $4, 6, 10$ 15. $0, 8, 8$

   $\underline{\hspace{0.7cm}} + \underline{\hspace{0.7cm}} = \underline{\hspace{0.7cm}}$ $\underline{\hspace{0.7cm}} + \underline{\hspace{0.7cm}} = \underline{\hspace{0.7cm}}$ $\underline{\hspace{0.7cm}} + \underline{\hspace{0.7cm}} = \underline{\hspace{0.7cm}}$

   $\underline{\hspace{0.7cm}} + \underline{\hspace{0.7cm}} = \underline{\hspace{0.7cm}}$ $\underline{\hspace{0.7cm}} + \underline{\hspace{0.7cm}} = \underline{\hspace{0.7cm}}$ $\underline{\hspace{0.7cm}} + \underline{\hspace{0.7cm}} = \underline{\hspace{0.7cm}}$

A number line can help you find the **difference**.

$9 - 3 = \underline{}6$

$$\begin{array}{r} 9 \\ -\ 3 \\ \hline 6 \end{array}$$

0 1 2 3 4 5 6 7 8 9 10

Write the **differences**.

1. $8 - 3 = \underline{}$ 2. $7 - 2 = \underline{}$ 3. $10 - 4 = \underline{}$

4. $9 - 1 = \underline{}$ 5. $6 - 0 = \underline{}$ 6. $8 - 4 = \underline{}$

7. $$\begin{array}{r} 6 \\ -\ 4 \\ \hline \end{array}$$ 8. $$\begin{array}{r} 8 \\ -\ 2 \\ \hline \end{array}$$ 9. $$\begin{array}{r} 5 \\ -\ 5 \\ \hline \end{array}$$ 10. $$\begin{array}{r} 9 \\ -\ 4 \\ \hline \end{array}$$

11. $$\begin{array}{r} 10 \\ -\ 3 \\ \hline \end{array}$$ 12. $$\begin{array}{r} 7 \\ -\ 4 \\ \hline \end{array}$$ 13. $$\begin{array}{r} 9 \\ -\ 7 \\ \hline \end{array}$$ 14. $$\begin{array}{r} 10 \\ -\ 8 \\ \hline \end{array}$$

15. Write a subtraction number sentence for this number line.

0 1 2 3 4 5 6 7 8 9 10

$\underline{} - \underline{} = \underline{}$

Look at these subtraction facts:

_____ _____

_____ _____

When you know one fact, you can think of another fact.

Write the **differences**.

1. 7 – 3 = _____   2. 9 – 5 = _____   3. 7 – 0 = _____

   7 – 4 = _____   9 – 4 = _____   7 – 7 = _____

4. 9 – 1 = _____   5. 10 – 2 = _____   6. 8 – 6 = _____

   9 – 8 = _____   10 – 8 = _____   8 – 2 = _____

Write the **difference** and another subtraction fact that uses the same numbers.

7. 9 – 5 = _____   8. 7 – 5 = _____   9. 6 – 0 = _____

_____ – _____ = _____   _____ – _____ = _____   _____ – _____ = _____

10. 10 – 2 = _____   11. 8 – 8 = _____   12. 8 – 1 = _____

_____ – _____ = _____   _____ – _____ = _____   _____ – _____ = _____

Use each group of numbers to write subtraction facts.

13.   3, 6, 9   14.   2, 8, 10   15.   0, 9, 9

_____ – _____ = _____   _____ – _____ = _____   _____ – _____ = _____

_____ – _____ = _____   _____ – _____ = _____   _____ – _____ = _____

SUBTRACTION FUN

Write the **differences**.
Color the picture.

$$6 - 6$$

$$10 - 8$$

$$6 - 2$$

$$7 - 4$$

$$8 - 4$$

$$8 - 8$$

$$9 - 5$$

$$4 - 4$$

$$7 - 2$$

$$9 - 4$$

$$6 - 1$$

$$10 - 6$$

$$9 - 6$$

$$8 - 6$$

$$10 - 9$$

$$7 - 3$$

$$8 - 5$$

$$10 - 5$$

0 = Red

1 = Purple

2 = Blue

3 = Orange

4 = Yellow

5 = Green

Add
+

Subtract
−

Watch out for the signs!

If you are adding, write the **sum**. If you are subtracting, write the **difference**.

1. $8 + 1 =$ _____

2. $7 - 2 =$ _____

3. $9 + 0 =$ _____

4. $10 - 1 =$ _____

5. $6 + 3 =$ _____

6. $8 - 3 =$ _____

7. $8 - 0 =$ _____

8. $7 + 2 =$ _____

9. $4 + 6 =$ _____

B-e-e-e-e sure to watch those signs!

10.
$$\begin{array}{r} 1 \\ + \ 9 \\ \hline \end{array}$$

11.
$$\begin{array}{r} 5 \\ - \ 1 \\ \hline \end{array}$$

12.
$$\begin{array}{r} 7 \\ + \ 0 \\ \hline \end{array}$$

13.
$$\begin{array}{r} 9 \\ - \ 2 \\ \hline \end{array}$$

14.
$$\begin{array}{r} 3 \\ - \ 0 \\ \hline \end{array}$$

15.
$$\begin{array}{r} 3 \\ + \ 7 \\ \hline \end{array}$$

16.
$$\begin{array}{r} 5 \\ + \ 5 \\ \hline \end{array}$$

17.
$$\begin{array}{r} 6 \\ - \ 0 \\ \hline \end{array}$$

NUMBERS 11 THROUGH 20

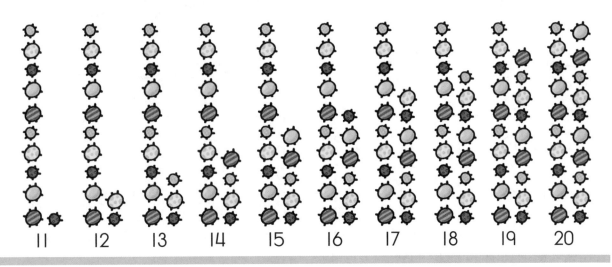

| 11 | 12 | 13 | 14 | 15 | 16 | 17 | 18 | 19 | 20 |

Match. The first one is done for you.

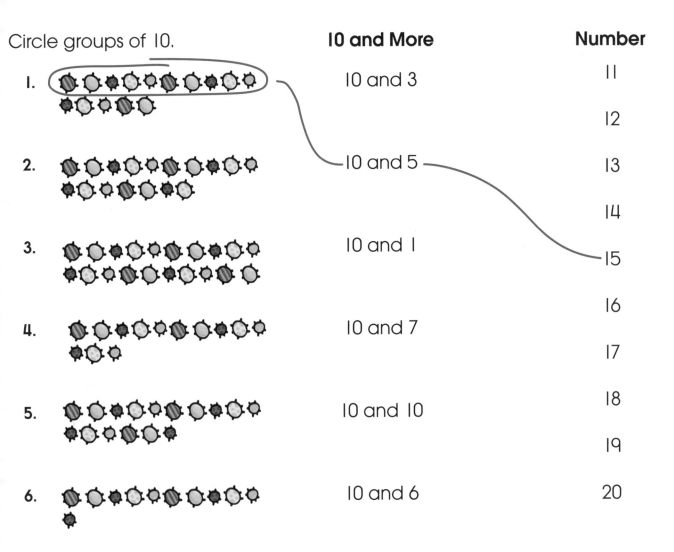

Circle groups of 10.

10 and More

Number

1.

10 and 3

11

12

2.

10 and 5

13

14

3.

10 and 1

15

16

4.

10 and 7

17

5.

10 and 10

18

19

6.

10 and 6

20

I through 10	1	2	3	4	5	6	7	8	9	10
11 and more	11	12	13	14	15	16	17	18	19	20

Write the missing numbers.

1. 11, 12, ____, 14, ____, 16, ____, 18, ____, 20

2. 11, ____, ____, ____, 15, ____, ____, ____, 19

3. 5, ____, ____, 8, ____, ____, 11, ____, ____, 14

4. ____, ____, 13, ____, ____, ____, 17, ____, ____, 20

5. Connect the dots.

__5__ + __6__ = __11__

Write an addition number sentence about the domino.

1.

_____ + _____ = _____

2.

_____ + _____ = _____

3.

_____ + _____ = _____

4.

_____ + _____ = _____

5.

_____ + _____ = _____

6.

_____ + _____ = _____

7. _____ + _____ = _____

8. _____ + _____ = _____

9. _____ + _____ = _____

Draw dots on the domino to find the **sum** for the problem. Write the **sum**.

10.

6 + 5 = _____

11.

6 + 6 = _____

12.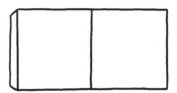

4 + 6 = _____

$$\begin{array}{r} 7 \\ + 3 \\ \hline 10 \end{array}$$

Write the **sums**.

1.
$$\begin{array}{r} 5 \\ + 6 \\ \hline \end{array}$$

2.
$$\begin{array}{r} 8 \\ + 3 \\ \hline \end{array}$$

3.
$$\begin{array}{r} 9 \\ + 1 \\ \hline \end{array}$$

4.
$$\begin{array}{r} 4 \\ + 4 \\ \hline \end{array}$$

5.
$$\begin{array}{r} 7 \\ + 5 \\ \hline \end{array}$$

6.
$$\begin{array}{r} 3 \\ + 9 \\ \hline \end{array}$$

7.
$$\begin{array}{r} 7 \\ + 2 \\ \hline \end{array}$$

8.
$$\begin{array}{r} 9 \\ + 2 \\ \hline \end{array}$$

9.
$$\begin{array}{r} 6 \\ + 6 \\ \hline \end{array}$$

10.
$$\begin{array}{r} 7 \\ + 4 \\ \hline \end{array}$$

11.
$$\begin{array}{r} 5 \\ + 5 \\ \hline \end{array}$$

12.
$$\begin{array}{r} 8 \\ + 4 \\ \hline \end{array}$$

$10 - 7 = \underline{\quad 3 \quad}$

$10 - 3 = \underline{\quad 7 \quad}$

Write the **differences**.

1. $10 - 2 = \underline{\qquad}$

   $10 - 8 = \underline{\qquad}$

2. $12 - 8 = \underline{\qquad}$

   $12 - 4 = \underline{\qquad}$

3. $12 - 3 = \underline{\qquad}$

   $12 - 9 = \underline{\qquad}$

4. $12 - 6 = \underline{\qquad}$

5. $12 - 5 = \underline{\qquad}$

   $12 - 7 = \underline{\qquad}$

6. $11 - 3 = \underline{\qquad}$

   $11 - 8 = \underline{\qquad}$

7. $11 - 4 = \underline{\qquad}$

   $11 - 7 = \underline{\qquad}$

8. $11 - 5 = \underline{\qquad}$

   $11 - 6 = \underline{\qquad}$

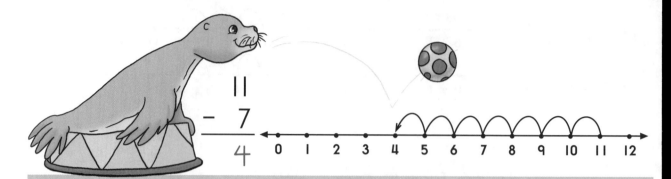

$$\begin{array}{r} 11 \\ -\ 7 \\ \hline 4 \end{array}$$

Write the **differences**.

1.
$$\begin{array}{r} 11 \\ -\ 5 \\ \hline \end{array}$$

2.
$$\begin{array}{r} 10 \\ -\ 4 \\ \hline \end{array}$$

3.
$$\begin{array}{r} 9 \\ -\ 5 \\ \hline \end{array}$$

4.
$$\begin{array}{r} 12 \\ -\ 6 \\ \hline \end{array}$$

5.
$$\begin{array}{r} 11 \\ -\ 3 \\ \hline \end{array}$$

6.
$$\begin{array}{r} 10 \\ -\ 2 \\ \hline \end{array}$$

7.
$$\begin{array}{r} 12 \\ -\ 4 \\ \hline \end{array}$$

8.
$$\begin{array}{r} 11 \\ -\ 2 \\ \hline \end{array}$$

9.
$$\begin{array}{r} 12 \\ -\ 7 \\ \hline \end{array}$$

10.
$$\begin{array}{r} 12 \\ -\ 5 \\ \hline \end{array}$$

11.
$$\begin{array}{r} 11 \\ -\ 4 \\ \hline \end{array}$$

12.
$$\begin{array}{r} 12 \\ -\ 8 \\ \hline \end{array}$$

DO YOU ADD OR SUBTRACT?

If you are adding, write the **sum**.
If you are subtracting, write the **difference**.

$$12 - 3$$

$$7 + 3$$

$$10 - 4$$

$$9 + 2$$

$$10 - 8$$

$$12 - 4$$

$$12 - 7$$

$$8 + 3$$

$$1 + 9$$

$$10 - 3$$

$$12 - 6$$

$$9 - 7$$

$$11 - 4$$

$$7 + 2$$

$$0 + 9$$

$$5 + 6$$

Follow the path around the animals that like water.
If you are adding, write the **sum**.
If you are subtracting, write the **difference**.
Some examples are done for you.

| 3 | + 2 | 5 | - 2 | 3 | + 4 | | + 3 | |
| - 1 |
| + 3 |

| | + 5 | | - 2 | | - 6 | |
| + 1 |
| | - 2 | | - 6 | |
| + 4 |
| 6 |

Circle the problems that equal each number.
The first one is done for you.

1. Circle the problems that equal 9.

(10 – 1)   (2 + 7)   (8 + 1)   3 + 5   11 – 3

2. Circle the problems that equal 5.

3 + 3   6 – 1   5 + 1   5 + 0   9 – 4

3. Circle the problems that equal 8.

10 – 2   4 + 4   6 + 3   2 + 6   12 – 6

4. Circle the problems that equal 10.

12 – 3   6 + 4   7 + 3   4 + 5   11 – 1

5. Circle the problems that equal 12.

4 + 7   12 – 0   8 + 4   7 + 5   6 + 5

6. Circle the problems that equal 6.

3 + 3   12 – 6   5 + 1   9 + 3   11 – 4

7. Circle the problems that equal 11.

6 + 4   9 + 2   5 + 6   7 + 5   8 + 3

8. Circle the problems that equal 7.

7 + 0   11 – 4   4 + 3   2 + 6   12 – 1

Write the **differences**.
Color the picture.

12 – 9 = _____ **Brown**

10 – 9 = _____ **Red**

11 – 9 = _____ Yellow

12 – 8 = _____ Green

12 – 6 = _____ **Blue**

11 – 6 = _____ **Black**

TENS & ONES

_____1_____ tens _____1_____ ones

How many? _____11_____

Count the objects. Circle the objects in groups of ten.
Write how many **tens** and **ones** there are. Then write the number.

1.

_____ tens _____ ones

How many? _____

2.

_____ tens _____ ones

How many? _____

3.

_____ tens _____ ones

How many? _____

4.

_____ tens _____ ones

How many? _____

5.

_____ tens _____ ones

How many? _____

6.

_____ tens _____ ones

How many? _____

MORE ABOUT TENS & ONES

_____2 tens   _____3 ones   tens ones _____2 3_____

Count the **tens** and **ones**. Write how many **tens** and **ones** there are.

1.

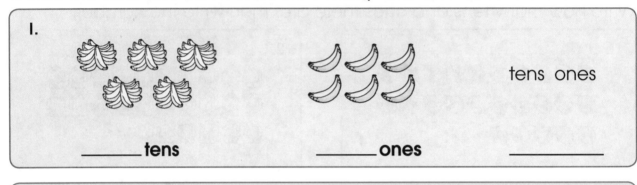

_____ tens   _____ ones   tens ones

_____

2.

_____ tens   _____ ones   tens ones

_____

3.

_____ tens   _____ ones   tens ones

_____

4.

_____ tens   _____ ones   tens ones

_____

Write the number.
Match the number to the correct picture.
The first one is done for you.

1. 2 tens   6 ones __26__

2. 4 tens   1 ones _____

3. 7 tens   0 ones _____

4. 5 tens   8 ones _____

5. 6 tens   2 ones _____

6. 8 tens   5 ones _____

7. 3 tens   7 ones _____

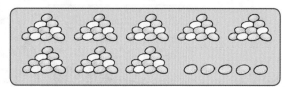

HOW MANY TENS & ONES ARE THERE?

Read each number.
Write how many **tens** and **ones** there are.
An example is done for you.

	tens	ones
1. 25	2	5
43	___	___
28	___	___
30	___	___
54	___	___
65	___	___

	tens	ones
2. 17	___	___
71	___	___
66	___	___
19	___	___
81	___	___
40	___	___

Count to **100**.
Write the missing numbers.

1									
2	12						72		
			33						
						64			
				45					
		26							
					58				
10					60				100

Count by **twos**. Circle those numbers.

WHICH NUMBERS ARE MISSING?

Write the missing numbers.

1. 1, 2, ____, 4, 5, ____, 7, ____, ____, 10

2. 41, ____, ____, ____, 45, 46, ____, 48, ____, 50

3. ____, 72, 73, ____, 75, ____, ____, 78, ____, ____

4. 31, ____, ____, ____, 35, ____, 37, ____, ____, ____

5. ____, ____, 83, ____, ____, ____, ____, 88, ____, 90

6. 61, ____, ____, ____, ____, ____, ____, ____, 69

7. 91, ____, 93, ____, ____, ____, ____, ____, 99, ____

Connect the dots.
Start at the ▲ and count by **ones** to **21**.
Start at the ■ and count by **tens** to **100**.

Count by **tens** to **100**. Write the missing numbers.

10   _____   30   _____   _____

_____   70   _____   _____

Write the number that comes **before**.
The first one is done for you.

1. _17_ 18   2. _____ 33

3. _____ 24   4. _____ 67

5. _____ 81   6. _____ 30

7. _____ 45   8. _____ 27

Write the number that comes **after**.
The first one is done for you.

9. 22 _23_   10. 11 _____

11. 18 _____   12. 37 _____

13. 27 _____   14. 6 _____

15. 38 _____   16. 69 _____

Write how many **tens** and **ones** there are in each group.
Then write the numbers. Circle the **greater** number.
The first one is done for you.

1.

__3__ tens __2__ ones   __2__ tens __3__ ones

(32)   __23__

2.

_____ tens _____ ones   _____ tens _____ ones

_____   _____

3.

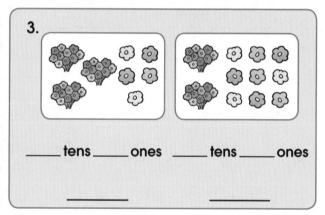

_____ tens _____ ones   _____ tens _____ ones

_____   _____

4.

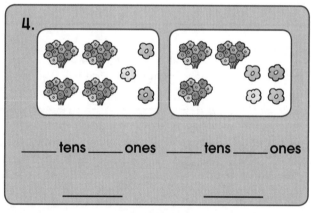

_____ tens _____ ones   _____ tens _____ ones

_____   _____

5.

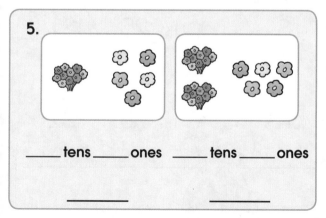

_____ tens _____ ones   _____ tens _____ ones

_____   _____

6.

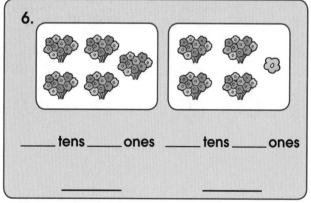

_____ tens _____ ones   _____ tens _____ ones

_____   _____

Circle the number that is **greater**.
The first one is done for you.

1. (23)   14   2. 50   48   3. 25   31

4. 19   21   5. 35   27   6. 10   15

7. 18   10   8. 13   31   9. 43   34

Circle the number that is **less**.
The first one is done for you.

10. 55   (48)   11. 25   31   12. 23   36

13. 62   59   14. 18   13   15. 25   31

16. 58   69   17. 44   54   18. 78   82

$$\begin{array}{r} 9 \\ + \ 4 \\ \hline 13 \end{array}$$

Write the **sums**.

1. $\begin{array}{r} 8 \\ + \ 5 \\ \hline \end{array}$

2. $\begin{array}{r} 7 \\ + \ 7 \\ \hline \end{array}$

3. $\begin{array}{r} 9 \\ + \ 6 \\ \hline \end{array}$

4. $\begin{array}{r} 8 \\ + \ 4 \\ \hline \end{array}$

5. $\begin{array}{r} 7 \\ + \ 6 \\ \hline \end{array}$

6. $\begin{array}{r} 5 \\ + \ 9 \\ \hline \end{array}$

7. $\begin{array}{r} 8 \\ + \ 7 \\ \hline \end{array}$

8. $\begin{array}{r} 6 \\ + \ 6 \\ \hline \end{array}$

9. $\begin{array}{r} 6 \\ + \ 8 \\ \hline \end{array}$

10. $\begin{array}{r} 7 \\ + \ 5 \\ \hline \end{array}$

11. $\begin{array}{r} 4 \\ + \ 9 \\ \hline \end{array}$

12. $\begin{array}{r} 8 \\ + \ 3 \\ \hline \end{array}$

13. $\begin{array}{r} 7 \\ + \ 4 \\ \hline \end{array}$

14. $\begin{array}{r} 9 \\ + \ 0 \\ \hline \end{array}$

15. $\begin{array}{r} 7 \\ + \ 8 \\ \hline \end{array}$

16. $\begin{array}{r} 5 \\ + \ 5 \\ \hline \end{array}$

Write the **sums**.

1. $6 + 7 =$ _____   2. $4 + 9 =$ _____   3. $6 + 6 =$ _____

4. $8 + 6 =$ _____   5. $7 + 5 =$ _____   6. $8 + 0 =$ _____

7. $7 + 8 =$ _____   8. $5 + 9 =$ _____   9. $7 + 7 =$ _____

Write the missing numbers.

10. $6 +$ _____ $= 14$ 11. $9 +$ _____ $= 15$ 12. $8 +$ _____ $= 12$

13. _____ $+ 7 = 13$ 14. $8 +$ _____ $= 8$ 15. _____ $+ 4 = 11$

16. $3 +$ _____ $= 10$ 17. $7 +$ _____ $= 15$ 18. _____ $+ 9 = 14$

MORE SUBTRACTION FACTS

Think of an addition fact to help you find the **difference**.

I know 6 + 8 = 14.

$14 - 6 = \underline{8}$

Write the **differences**.

1. $11 - 7 = \underline{}$ 2. $13 - 9 = \underline{}$ 3. $12 - 5 = \underline{}$

4. $15 - 9 = \underline{}$ 5. $10 - 9 = \underline{}$ 6. $14 - 7 = \underline{}$

7. $12 - 3 = \underline{}$ 8. $15 - 8 = \underline{}$ 9. $13 - 8 = \underline{}$

10. $14 - 5 = \underline{}$ 11. $13 - 6 = \underline{}$ 12. $7 - 0 = \underline{}$

13. $12 - 8 = \underline{}$ 14. $9 - 9 = \underline{}$ 15. $14 - 9 = \underline{}$

16. $15 - 7 = \underline{}$ 17. $13 - 5 = \underline{}$ 18. $11 - 2 = \underline{}$

If you are adding, write the **sum**. If you are subtracting, write the **difference**.

1. 9
    + 3

2. 11
    − 6

3. 8
    + 7

4. 11
    − 5

5. 12
    − 9

6. 14
    − 6

7. 8
    + 5

8. 0
    + 9

9. 9
    + 6

10. 12
    − 5

11. 13
    − 7

12. 12
    − 3

13. 14
    − 5

14. 9
    + 4

15. 8
    − 8

16. 7
    + 7

Here are four new addition facts to remember:

$8 + 8 = \underline{16}$ $8 + 9 = \underline{17}$

$9 + 7 = \underline{16}$ $9 + 9 = \underline{18}$

Write the **sums**.

1. $8 + 6 =$ _____   2. $8 + 7 =$ _____   3. $8 + 8 =$ _____

4. $7 + 7 =$ _____   5. $7 + 8 =$ _____   6. $7 + 9 =$ _____

7. $9 + 7 =$ _____   8. $9 + 8 =$ _____   9. $9 + 9 =$ _____

10.
$$\begin{array}{r} 8 \\ + 5 \\ \hline \end{array}$$

11.
$$\begin{array}{r} 6 \\ + 7 \\ \hline \end{array}$$

12.
$$\begin{array}{r} 9 \\ + 6 \\ \hline \end{array}$$

13.
$$\begin{array}{r} 7 \\ + 4 \\ \hline \end{array}$$

14.
$$\begin{array}{r} 9 \\ + 8 \\ \hline \end{array}$$

15.
$$\begin{array}{r} 9 \\ + 7 \\ \hline \end{array}$$

16.
$$\begin{array}{r} 6 \\ + 8 \\ \hline \end{array}$$

17.
$$\begin{array}{r} 9 \\ + 9 \\ \hline \end{array}$$

ADDITION NUMBER WHEELS

Fill in each addition number wheel.
Add the number in the center to each number in the middle.
The first one is done for you.

1.

2.

3.

4.

Color the picture.

Even numbers = Blue

Odd numbers = Red

Fill in the addition facts table by finding the **sums**.

+	0	1	2	3	4	5	6	7	8	9
0	0			3						
1								8		
2			4							
3										
4						9				
5									13	
6	6									
7				11						
8										
9			11			14				

Each of these addition facts can be called a **double**.
Write the **sums**.

1. $1 + 1 =$ _____ 2. $2 + 2 =$ _____ 3. $3 + 3 =$ _____

4. $4 + 4 =$ _____ 5. $5 + 5 =$ _____ 6. $6 + 6 =$ _____

7. $7 + 7 =$ _____ 8. $8 + 8 =$ _____ 9. $9 + 9 =$ _____

DOUBLES & MORE

If you know a **double**, it's easy to remember a **double plus 1** fact.

$7 + 7 = \underline{14}$

$7 + 8 = \underline{15}$

Write the **sums**. Use the addition facts table on page 229 if you need help.

1. $4 + 4 = \underline{\hspace{1cm}}$ 2. $6 + 6 = \underline{\hspace{1cm}}$ 3. $8 + 8 = \underline{\hspace{1cm}}$

$4 + 5 = \underline{\hspace{1cm}}$ $6 + 7 = \underline{\hspace{1cm}}$ $8 + 9 = \underline{\hspace{1cm}}$

4. $5 + 5 = \underline{\hspace{1cm}}$ 5. $3 + 3 = \underline{\hspace{1cm}}$ 6. $7 + 7 = \underline{\hspace{1cm}}$

$5 + 6 = \underline{\hspace{1cm}}$ $3 + 4 = \underline{\hspace{1cm}}$ $7 + 8 = \underline{\hspace{1cm}}$

7.
$$\begin{array}{r} 6 \\ + 6 \\ \hline \end{array} \qquad \begin{array}{r} 6 \\ + 7 \\ \hline \end{array}$$

8.
$$\begin{array}{r} 7 \\ + 7 \\ \hline \end{array} \qquad \begin{array}{r} 7 \\ + 8 \\ \hline \end{array}$$

9.
$$\begin{array}{r} 5 \\ + 5 \\ \hline \end{array} \qquad \begin{array}{r} 5 \\ + 6 \\ \hline \end{array}$$

10.
$$\begin{array}{r} 8 \\ + 8 \\ \hline \end{array} \qquad \begin{array}{r} 8 \\ + 9 \\ \hline \end{array}$$

MORE SUBTRACTION FACTS

Look at these subtraction facts:

$16 - 9 = \underline{7}$
$16 - 7 = \underline{9}$

When you know one fact, you can think of another fact.

Write the **differences**.

1. $12 - 3 = \underline{\hphantom{00}}$ 2. $14 - 5 = \underline{\hphantom{00}}$ 3. $15 - 7 = \underline{\hphantom{00}}$

$12 - 9 = \underline{\hphantom{00}}$ $14 - 9 = \underline{\hphantom{00}}$ $15 - 8 = \underline{\hphantom{00}}$

4. $17 - 9 = \underline{\hphantom{00}}$ 5. $13 - 5 = \underline{\hphantom{00}}$ 6. $11 - 6 = \underline{\hphantom{00}}$

$17 - 8 = \underline{\hphantom{00}}$ $13 - 8 = \underline{\hphantom{00}}$ $11 - 5 = \underline{\hphantom{00}}$

Write the **difference**.
Write another fact that uses the same numbers.

7. $14 - 6 = \underline{\hphantom{00}}$ 8. $17 - 8 = \underline{\hphantom{00}}$ 9. $12 - 9 = \underline{\hphantom{00}}$

$\underline{\hphantom{0}} - \underline{\hphantom{0}} = \underline{\hphantom{0}}$ $\underline{\hphantom{0}} - \underline{\hphantom{0}} = \underline{\hphantom{0}}$ $\underline{\hphantom{0}} - \underline{\hphantom{0}} = \underline{\hphantom{0}}$

10. $15 - 7 = \underline{\hphantom{00}}$ 11. $13 - 4 = \underline{\hphantom{00}}$ 12. $15 - 9 = \underline{\hphantom{00}}$

$\underline{\hphantom{0}} - \underline{\hphantom{0}} = \underline{\hphantom{0}}$ $\underline{\hphantom{0}} - \underline{\hphantom{0}} = \underline{\hphantom{0}}$ $\underline{\hphantom{0}} - \underline{\hphantom{0}} = \underline{\hphantom{0}}$

SUBTRACTION PUZZLES

Fill in the squares in the diamond puzzles.
An example is done for you.

FACT FAMILIES

$8 + 7 = \underline{15}$ $15 - 7 = \underline{8}$

$7 + 8 = \underline{15}$ $15 - 8 = \underline{7}$

The addition and subtraction facts are related in a **fact family**. All of the facts use the same numbers.

Write the missing numbers.

1. $4 + 7 = \underline{}$

   $7 + 4 = \underline{}$

   $11 - 4 = \underline{}$

   $11 - 7 = \underline{}$

2. $9 + 7 = \underline{}$

   $7 + 9 = \underline{}$

   $16 - 7 = \underline{}$

   $16 - 9 = \underline{}$

3. $7 + 0 = \underline{}$

   $0 + 7 = \underline{}$

   $7 - 0 = \underline{}$

   $7 - 7 = \underline{}$

4. $8 + 5 = \underline{}$

   $5 + \underline{} = 13$

   $13 - 5 = \underline{}$

   $13 - 8 = \underline{}$

5. $8 + 9 = \underline{}$

   $9 + 8 = \underline{}$

   $\underline{} - 9 = 8$

   $\underline{} - 8 = 9$

6. $9 + 9 = \underline{}$

   $18 - 9 = \underline{}$

Use the numbers to write addition and subtraction facts.

7. 6, 9, 15

   $\underline{} + \underline{} = \underline{}$

   $\underline{} + \underline{} = \underline{}$

   $\underline{} - \underline{} = \underline{}$

   $\underline{} - \underline{} = \underline{}$

8. 9, 9, 0

   $\underline{} + \underline{} = \underline{}$

   $\underline{} + \underline{} = \underline{}$

   $\underline{} - \underline{} = \underline{}$

   $\underline{} - \underline{} = \underline{}$

9. 5, 7, 12

   $\underline{} + \underline{} = \underline{}$

   $\underline{} + \underline{} = \underline{}$

   $\underline{} - \underline{} = \underline{}$

   $\underline{} - \underline{} = \underline{}$

ADDING THREE NUMBERS

Add any two numbers first. Then add the third number to find the **sum**.

Look for a ten
or a double.

Look for a **ten**.
Adding **10** to a
number is easy
to do!

$$\begin{array}{r} 4 \\ 6 \\ + 4 \\ \hline 14 \end{array}$$ 10

$$\begin{array}{r} 4 \\ 6 \\ + 4 \\ \hline 14 \end{array}$$ 8

Look for a **double**.
Add the third
number to it.

Write the **sums**.

1.
$$\begin{array}{r} 3 \\ 4 \\ + 4 \\ \hline \end{array}$$

2.
$$\begin{array}{r} 5 \\ 3 \\ + 5 \\ \hline \end{array}$$

3.
$$\begin{array}{r} 3 \\ 7 \\ + 7 \\ \hline \end{array}$$

4.
$$\begin{array}{r} 2 \\ 9 \\ + 2 \\ \hline \end{array}$$

5.
$$\begin{array}{r} 4 \\ 4 \\ + 2 \\ \hline \end{array}$$

6.
$$\begin{array}{r} 3 \\ 9 \\ + 3 \\ \hline \end{array}$$

7.
$$\begin{array}{r} 4 \\ 4 \\ + 4 \\ \hline \end{array}$$

8.
$$\begin{array}{r} 3 \\ 4 \\ + 7 \\ \hline \end{array}$$

9.
$$\begin{array}{r} 5 \\ 7 \\ + 5 \\ \hline \end{array}$$

10.
$$\begin{array}{r} 8 \\ 0 \\ + 8 \\ \hline \end{array}$$

NUMBER RIDDLES

Read the problem. Find the number.
Use the space to show your work.

1. Start with 3.
   Double it.
   Add 8.
   What is the number? _____

2. Start with 5.
   Add 3.
   Add 9.
   What is the number? _____

3. Start with 8.
   Subtract 7.
   Add 3.
   Double it.
   What is the number? _____

4. Start with 8.
   Subtract 5.
   Add 1.
   Subtract 4.
   What is the number? _____

5. Start with 4.
   Double it.
   Double it.
   What is the number? _____

RACE TO THE FINISH!

This race is for 2 players.
Take turns giving the answer to every other problem.
The player who has more correct answers is the winner.

3 tens + 7 ones = ____

Start

$$\begin{array}{r} 3 \\ + 9 \\ \hline \end{array}$$

$$\begin{array}{r} 6 \\ - 3 \\ \hline \end{array}$$

$$\begin{array}{r} 8 \\ + 7 \\ \hline \end{array}$$

$$\begin{array}{r} 14 \\ - 5 \\ \hline \end{array}$$

$$\begin{array}{r} 9 \\ + 8 \\ \hline \end{array}$$

$$\begin{array}{r} 12 \\ - 4 \\ \hline \end{array}$$

____ 85 ____

$$\begin{array}{r} 8 \\ - 6 \\ \hline \end{array}$$

$$\begin{array}{r} 15 \\ - \square \\ \hline 6 \end{array}$$

$$\begin{array}{r} 8 \\ + 4 \\ \hline \end{array}$$

$$\begin{array}{r} 12 \\ - 3 \\ \hline \end{array}$$

$$\begin{array}{r} 9 \\ + 7 \\ \hline \end{array}$$

$$\begin{array}{r} 6 \\ + \square \\ \hline 15 \end{array}$$

$$\begin{array}{r} 12 \\ - 7 \\ \hline \end{array}$$

$$\begin{array}{r} 9 \\ + 5 \\ \hline \end{array}$$

$$\begin{array}{r} 8 \\ + 0 \\ \hline \end{array}$$

$$\begin{array}{r} 12 \\ - \square \\ \hline 3 \end{array}$$

$$\begin{array}{r} 10 \\ - 3 \\ \hline \end{array}$$

6 tens + 4 ones = ____

$$\begin{array}{r} 8 \\ + 8 \\ \hline \end{array}$$

$$\begin{array}{r} 15 \\ - \square \\ \hline 9 \end{array}$$

$$\begin{array}{r} 14 \\ - 5 \\ \hline \end{array}$$

$$\begin{array}{r} 13 \\ - \square \\ \hline 7 \end{array}$$

$$\begin{array}{r} 11 \\ - 7 \\ \hline \end{array}$$

$$\begin{array}{r} 9 \\ + 9 \\ \hline \end{array}$$

$$\begin{array}{r} 10 \\ + 6 \\ \hline \end{array}$$

$$\begin{array}{r} 16 \\ - \square \\ \hline 7 \end{array}$$

$$\begin{array}{r} 6 \\ + \square \\ \hline 14 \end{array}$$

$$\begin{array}{r} 9 \\ + \square \\ \hline 12 \end{array}$$

$$\begin{array}{r} 14 \\ - \square \\ \hline 5 \end{array}$$

Finish

Write **how many** there are.

1. _____

2. _____

Circle groups of ten. Count the ones. Write **how many** there are.

3. _____ tens _____ ones = _____

4. _____ tens _____ one = _____

5. Count the objects in each group. Write the numbers.
   Circle the number that is **less**.

_____   _____

Circle the number that is **greater**.

6. 29   37   7. 43   34   8. 69   70

Write the missing numbers.

9. 31, ___, 33, ___, ___, ___, 37, ___, 39, ___

10. 75, ___, ___, 78, ___, ___, 81, ___, ___, 84

WHAT I LEARNED ABOUT FACTS

Write the **sums**.

1. $5 + 6 =$ _____

2. $4 + 8 =$ _____

3. $9 + 9 =$ _____

4. $7 + 0 =$ _____

5. $8 + 9 =$ _____

6. $8 + 6 =$ _____

Subtract to find the **differences**.

7. $13 - 8 =$ _____

8. $5 - 5 =$ _____

9. $14 - 7 =$ _____

10. $16 - 9 =$ _____

11. $14 - 5 =$ _____

12. $15 - 8 =$ _____

If you are adding, write the **sum**.
If you are subtracting, write the **difference**.

13.
$$\begin{array}{r} 12 \\ - 5 \\ \hline \end{array}$$

14.
$$\begin{array}{r} 4 \\ + 9 \\ \hline \end{array}$$

15.
$$\begin{array}{r} 8 \\ - 0 \\ \hline \end{array}$$

16.
$$\begin{array}{r} 15 \\ - 6 \\ \hline \end{array}$$

17.
$$\begin{array}{r} 6 \\ + 6 \\ \hline \end{array}$$

18.
$$\begin{array}{r} 16 \\ - 8 \\ \hline \end{array}$$

19.
$$\begin{array}{r} 3 \\ 6 \\ + 7 \\ \hline \end{array}$$

20.
$$\begin{array}{r} 6 \\ 8 \\ + 4 \\ \hline \end{array}$$

21. Write a fact family for these numbers: **7**, **9**, and **16**.

_____ + _____ = _____   _____ - _____ = _____

_____ + _____ = _____   _____ - _____ = _____

Penny 1¢   **1 cent**

When we count pennies, we count by ones.

Nickel 5¢   **5 cents**

When we count nickels, we count by fives.
1 nickel = 5 pennies

Dime 10¢   **10 cents**

When we count dimes, we count by tens.
1 dime = 10 pennies
         2 nickels

Quarter 25¢   **25 cents**

1 quarter = 25 pennies
            5 nickels
            2 dimes and 1 nickel

I penny = 1¢

 I nickel = 5¢

5 pennies are the same as 1 nickel.

Count the money. Write the amounts.

1.

_____ _____ _____ _____   _____ ¢

2.

_____ _____ _____   _____ ¢

3.

_____ _____ _____ _____ _____   _____ ¢

4.

_____ _____   _____ ¢

Count by fives.
Then count on by ones.

| 5¢ | 10¢ | 11¢ | 12¢ | 13¢ | 14¢ | 15¢ |

Count the money. Write the amounts.

1.

_____ _____ _____ _____ _____ _____   _____ ¢

2.

_____ _____ _____ _____   _____ ¢

3.

_____ _____ _____ _____ _____   _____ ¢

4.

_____ _____ _____ _____ _____ _____   _____ ¢

| 5¢ | 10¢ | 15¢ | 20¢ |

Count the money.
Write the amounts.

1.

_____ ¢

2.

_____ ¢

3.

_____ ¢

4.

_____ ¢

5.

_____ ¢

6.

_____ ¢

1 dime = 10¢

10 pennies are the same as 1 dime.

Count the money. Write the amounts.

1.

_____ _____ _____ _____ ¢

2.

_____ _____ _____ _____ _____ ¢

3.

_____ _____ _____ _____ _____ _____ _____ ¢

4.

_____ _____ _____ _____ _____ _____ _____ _____ ¢

<u>10¢</u>   <u>20¢</u>   <u>30¢</u>   <u>40¢</u>

Count the money.
Write the amounts.

1.

_____ ¢

2.

_____ ¢

3.

_____ ¢

4.

_____ ¢

5.

_____ ¢

6.

_____ ¢

Count by tens, fives, and ones.

__10¢__   __15¢__   __16¢__

Count the money. Write the prices.

1.

_____ _____ _____ _____

2.

_____ _____ _____ _____

3.

_____ _____ _____ _____ _____

4.

_____ _____ _____ _____ _____ _____

Count the coins and write each amount on each line.
Is there enough money to pay for each item? Circle **yes** or **no**.

1.

_____ ¢   Can you buy the flowers?
            yes   **no**

2.

_____ ¢   Can you buy the banana?
            yes   **no**

3.

_____ ¢   Can you buy the grapes?
            yes   **no**

4.

Can you buy the
strawberries?

_____ ¢   **yes**   **no**

5.

_____ ¢   Can you buy the apple?
            yes   **no**

6.

_____ ¢   Can you buy the orange?
            yes   **no**

Match.

16¢

25¢

37¢

19¢

24¢

COUNTING MONEY

Circle the coins needed to buy the toys.
The first one is done for you.

1.

2.

3.

4.

5.

6.

1 quarter = 25¢

1 quarter is equal to 25 pennies.

Count the money. Write the amounts.

1.

_____ _____ _____ _____   _____ ¢

2.

_____ _____ _____ _____ _____   _____ ¢

3.

_____ _____ _____ _____   _____ ¢

4.

_____ _____ _____ _____ _____ _____   _____ ¢

COUNTING MONEY

Count the money. Write the prices.

1.

——— ——— ——— ———

2.

——— ——— ——— ———

3.

——— ——— ——— ——— ———

4.

——— ——— ——— ——— ———

5.

——— ——— ———

COUNTING MONEY

Count each group of coins. Write the amounts.
Cross out the groups that are not equal to a quarter.

1. _____ ¢

2. _____ ¢

3. _____ ¢

4. _____ ¢

25¢

5. _____ ¢

6. _____ ¢

ADDING AMOUNTS OF MONEY

What is the price of each toy?
Add the amounts to find the total cost.
The first one is done for you.

1.

$$\begin{array}{r} 32¢ \\ + \ 50¢ \\ \hline 82¢ \end{array}$$

What is the total?   82¢

2.

$$\begin{array}{r} \underline{} \\ + \ \underline{} \\ \hline \end{array}$$

What is the total?   _____ ¢

3.

$$\begin{array}{r} \underline{} \\ + \ \underline{} \\ \hline \end{array}$$

What is the total?   _____ ¢

4.

$$\begin{array}{r} \underline{} \\ + \ \underline{} \\ \hline \end{array}$$

What is the total?   _____ ¢

5.

$$\begin{array}{r} \underline{} \\ + \ \underline{} \\ \hline \end{array}$$

What is the total?   _____ ¢

6.

$$\begin{array}{r} \underline{} \\ + \ \underline{} \\ \hline \end{array}$$

What is the total?   _____ ¢

COUNTING THE MINUTES IN AN HOUR

It takes the minute hand **5** minutes to move from one number to the next.

Count the minutes by **fives**.
Write the minutes on each line.
The first one is done for you.

How many minutes are in an hour? _____

A clock has two hands. The short hand shows the hour.
When the long hand points to the **12**, we say "**o'clock.**"

hour hand

minute hand

The hour hand points to the **2**.
The minute hand points to the **12**.

The time is **2 o'clock** or **2:00**.
We can say: "**two o'clock.**"

Read the hour hand first. Then read the minute hand.
Write the time in two ways. The first one is done for you.

1.

___3___ o'clock

___3:00___

2.

_____ o'clock

_____:_____

3.

_____ o'clock

_____:_____

4.

_____ o'clock

_____:_____

5.

_____ o'clock

_____:_____

6.

_____ o'clock

_____:_____

The long hand tells the minutes. When the minute hand points to the **6**, we say that it is **half past** the hour. The minute hand is *halfway* around the clock. The hour hand is *halfway* between the hour numbers.

The hour hand is halfway between the **2** and the **3**. The minute hand points to the **6**.

The time is **half past 2** or **2:30**.

It is **30** minutes after **2**. It is **2:30**.

We can say: **"two thirty."**

Read the hour hand first. Then read the minute hand.
Write the time in two ways. The first one is done for you.

1.

Half past___4___

___4:30___

2.

Half past_____

_____:_____

3.

Half past_____

_____:_____

4.

Half past_____

_____:_____

5.

Half past_____

_____:_____

6.

Half past_____

_____:_____

Write the times.

1.

_____ : _____

2.

_____ : _____

3.

_____ : _____

4.

_____ : _____

5.

_____ : _____

6.

_____ : _____

Draw a line to match the TV show to the correct clock.

5:00 Cowboy Sam

5:30 Dinosaurs!

7:00 Joke Time

7:30 Camp Talk

LEARNING ABOUT QUARTER PAST THE HOUR

When the minute hand points to the **3**, it is a quarter of the way around the clock. It is a **quarter past** the hour. The hour hand is a little past the hour number.

The time is quarter past **2**.

It is **15** minutes after **2**.
It is **2:15**.

We can say: "**quarter after 2**."

Read the hour hand first. Then read the minute hand.
Write the time in two ways. The first one is done for you.

1.

Quarter past ___6___

___6:15___

2.

Quarter past _____

_____:_____

3.

Quarter past _____

_____:_____

4.

Quarter past _____

_____:_____

5.

Quarter past _____

_____:_____

6.

Quarter past _____

_____:_____

LEARNING ABOUT QUARTER TO THE HOUR

When the minute hand points to the **9**, it is a **quarter to** the next hour. The hour hand is closer to the next hour.

The time is **quarter to 3**.
It is **15** minutes to **3**.
We can say: "**quarter to 3**."

OR

It is **45** minutes after **2**.
It is **2:45**.
We can say: "**two forty-five**."

Read the hour hand first. Then read the minute hand.
Write the time in two ways. The first one is done for you.

1.

Quarter to ___12___

_____11:45_____

2.

Quarter to _____

_____:_____

3.

Quarter to _____

_____:_____

4.

Quarter to _____

_____:_____

5.

Quarter to _____

_____:_____

6.

Quarter to _____

_____:_____

TELLING TIME

An **analog clock** has a minute hand and an hour hand. A **digital clock** shows the time this way: **5:00**. Look at your watch. Is it an analog or a digital watch?

Analog Clock

Digital Clock

FUN TIDBIT:

Did you know that digital clocks go back to the early 1900s? Some were called Plato clocks.

Read the digital clocks. Write the times.
The first one is done for you.

1.

2:15

2.

___:___

3.

___:___

4.

___:___

5.

___:___

6.

___:___

7.

___:___

8.

___:___

9.

___:___

Write the name of each animal under the clock that shows when it will see the doctor.

1.

   ____ : ____

2.

   ____ : ____

3.

   ____ : ____

4.

   ____ : ____

5.

   ____ : ____

6.

   ____ : ____

Bailey 1:30

Squawk 12:45

Mia 2:00

Fluffy 1:15

Pookie 4:45

Toby 4:15

TELLING TIME

Write the times. The first one is done for you.

1. __1:45__

2. ____:____

3. ____:____

4. ____:____

5. ____:____

6. ____:____

Draw hands on the clock faces to show the times.
The first one is done for you.

7. 2:45

8. 6:15

9. 9:45

10. 10:45

11. 3:15

12. 12:15

Write the times.

1.

_____ : _____

2.

_____ : _____

3.

_____ : _____

4.

_____ : _____

5.

_____ : _____

6.

_____ : _____

Draw hands on the clock faces to show the times.

7.

3:50

8.

12:00

9.

7:15

10.

12:50

11.

8:30

12.

2:45

Write the times.

1.

_____

2.

_____

3.

_____

4.

_____

5.

_____

6.

_____

Draw hands on the clock faces to show the times.

7.

3:45

8.

5:15

9.

1:45

10.

11:45

11.

4:15

12.

8:15

Write the times. The first one is done for you.

1.

1:30

2.
___:___

3.
___:___

4.

___:___

5.

___:___

6.

___:___

Draw hands on the clock faces to show the times.
The first one is done for you.

7.

6:30

8.

8:00

9.

1:00

10.

11:30

11.

5:00

12.

2:30

Movieland Cinema

Daffy Dino	1:30	Mystery Mouse	4:30
Cats in Space	2:45	Henry's Horse	5:15
Five Finny Fish	3:45	Mooove, Cow!	6:00

Draw hands on the clock faces to show the movie times.
Then write the times.

1.

_____

2.

_____

3.

_____

4.

_____

5.

_____

6.

_____

DETERMINING A.M. OR P.M.

There are 24 hours in a day.
The 24 hours of the day are divided into two periods called a.m. and p.m.

12	1	2	3	4	5	6	7	8	9	10	11	12	1	2	3	4	5	6	7	8	9	10	11	12
midnight												noon												midnight

a.m. ▬▬▬▬▬▬▬▬▬▬▬▬ p.m. ▬▬▬▬▬▬▬▬▬▬▬▬ a.m.

When would this happen?
Circle a.m. or p.m.

1. Waking up

7:00   a.m.   p.m.

2. Walking the dog

3:00   a.m.   p.m.

3. Playing soccer

4:00   a.m.   p.m.

4. Being in class

10:00   a.m.   p.m.

5. Eating lunch

12:00   a.m.   p.m.

6. Sleeping

12:00   a.m.   p.m.

Equal parts are the same size and shape.
Look at the shapes. One shape has 2 equal parts.

These are not equal.

2 Equal Parts

2 Unequal Parts

Circle the shapes that have equal parts.

1.

2.

3.

4.

5.

6.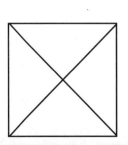

LEARNING ABOUT HALVES

Look at the shape. It has 2 equal parts. Each part is $\frac{1}{2}$ or **one-half**.

$\frac{1}{2}$ ←parts colored

$\frac{1}{2}$ ←equal parts

$\frac{1}{2}$ is a **fraction**.

A **fraction** is a number that tells about part of a shape or group.

Write the fraction $\frac{1}{2}$ on each part. The first one is done for you.

1.

$\frac{1}{2}$
$\frac{1}{2}$

2.

3.

4.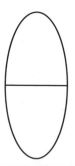

Color $\frac{1}{2}$ of each shape. The first one is done for you.

5.

6.

7.

8.

9.

10.

11.

12.

LEARNING ABOUT THIRDS

Look at the shape. It has 3 equal parts. Each part is $\frac{1}{3}$ or **one-third**.

$$\boxed{\frac{1}{3} \mid \frac{1}{3} \mid \frac{1}{3}}$$

$\frac{1}{3}$ ← parts colored

$\frac{1}{3}$ ← equal parts

Write the fraction $\frac{1}{3}$ on each part.

1.

2.

3.

4.
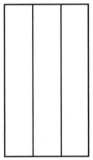

Color $\frac{1}{3}$ of each shape.

5.

6.

7.

8.

9.

10.

11.

12.
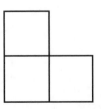

LEARNING ABOUT FOURTHS

Look at the shape. It has 4 equal parts. Each part is $\frac{1}{4}$ or **one-fourth**.

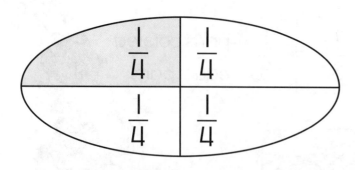

$\frac{1}{4}$ ←parts colored

$\frac{1}{4}$ ←equal parts

Write the fraction $\frac{1}{4}$ on each part.

1.

2.

3.

4.
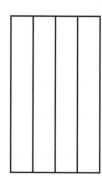

Color $\frac{1}{4}$ of each shape.

5.

6.

7.

8.

9.

10.

11.

12.
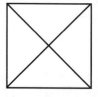

In a fraction, the top number tells how many parts are colored. The bottom number of a fraction tells how many equal parts there are in all.

$$\frac{1}{2} \qquad \frac{1}{3} \qquad \frac{1}{4}$$

Write the fraction to tell about the colored part of each shape. The first one is done for you.

1.

$$\frac{1}{2}$$

2.

$$\frac{}{3}$$

3.

4.

5.

6.

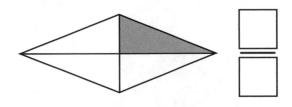

A fraction tells how many parts of a whole are being used. These fractions tell about the colored part of each shape.

$\dfrac{1}{2}$

$\dfrac{2}{3}$ ←parts colored
←equal parts

$\dfrac{3}{4}$

Write the fraction to tell about the colored part of each shape. The first one is done for you.

1.

$\dfrac{2}{4}$

2.

$\dfrac{3}{}$

3.

4.

5.

6.

$\frac{2}{3}$ ←parts colored

$\frac{2}{3}$ ←equal parts

Color the correct number of parts to show each fraction.

1. $\frac{1}{2}$

2. $\frac{2}{3}$

3. $\frac{4}{6}$

4. $\frac{1}{4}$

5. $\frac{5}{6}$

6. $\frac{3}{4}$

7. $\frac{3}{8}$

8. $\frac{2}{2}$

9. $\frac{2}{5}$

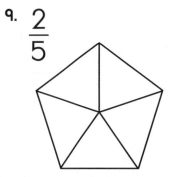

What parts of the groups are colored? Write the fractions.

1.

2.

3.

4.

5.

6.

7.

8.

SHOWING FRACTIONS

Color the objects to show the fractions.

1.

$\frac{2}{3}$

2.

$\frac{1}{2}$

3.

$\frac{3}{4}$

4.

$\frac{5}{8}$

5.

$\frac{4}{5}$

6.

$\frac{1}{5}$

7.

$\frac{7}{8}$

8.

$\frac{5}{6}$

Write the fractions for the shaded parts.

1.

2.

3.

4.

5.

6.

MAKING EQUAL SHARES

Show how to make equal shares by cutting each food item into the correct number of pieces. The first one is done for you.

1. You want to share a ham sandwich with a friend. How will the sandwich look?

2. You want to share a pizza with 7 friends. How will the pizza look?

3. You want to share a slice of watermelon with 2 friends. How will the watermelon look?

4. You want to share a sub sandwich with 3 friends. How will the sub sandwich look?

5. You want to share a licorice stick with a friend. How will the licorice stick look?

6. You want to share a pancake with 2 friends. How will the pancake look?

7. You want to share a cookie with 3 friends. How will the cookie look?

8. You want to share a birthday cake with 11 friends. How will the cake look?

The whole group is 4 cows.

Remember:
A half is one of
two equal parts.

$\frac{1}{2}$ $\frac{1}{2}$ Half of the group is 2 cows.

Circle half of the objects in each group.

1.

2.

3.

4.

5.

6.

SHOWING FRACTIONS

Color the object or objects to show each fraction.

1. $\dfrac{1}{2}$

2. $\dfrac{3}{4}$

3. $\dfrac{2}{3}$

4. $\dfrac{7}{8}$

5. $\dfrac{2}{5}$

6. $\dfrac{1}{4}$

7. $\dfrac{1}{8}$

8. $\dfrac{5}{6}$

Read and solve each word problem.
The first one is done for you.

1. The kids built **6** snowmen.
   Later, they built **5** more snowmen.
   How many snowmen were
   there **altogether**?

Solve

$$
\begin{array}{r}
6 \\
(+)\ 5 \\
\hline
11
\end{array}
$$ ___ snowmen

2. There were **11** hats.
   There were **4** scarves.
   How many **more** hats than scarves were there?

Solve

◯ _____

_____ hats

3. There were **4** sleds at the top of the hill.
   6 sleds were at the bottom of the hill.
   What was the **total** number of sleds?

Solve

◯ _____

_____ sleds

4. There were **11** cups of hot chocolate.
   The kids drank **5** cups.
   How many cups of hot chocolate were **left**?

Solve

◯ _____

_____ cups

ADDITION & SUBTRACTION WORD PROBLEMS

Match the picture word problems to the correct number sentences.
The first one is done for you.

1. How many bees are **left**?

$4 + 3 = 7$

2. How many birds are **left**?

$7 - 3 = 4$

3. How many butterflies are there **in all**?

$2 + 5 = 7$

4. How many ducks are **left**?

$6 - 2 = 4$

5. What is the **total** number of owls?

$5 - 3 = 2$

   Choosing the Operation to Solve Word Problems

Circle the correct questions and number sentences for the word problems
The first one is done for you.

1. **6** dragonflies were in the forest.
   3 dragonflies flew away.

   How many dragonflies were there in all? $6 + 3 = 9$

   ⟨How many dragonflies were left?⟩   ⟨$6 - 3 = 3$⟩

2. **10** butterflies were in the park.
   4 butterflies came along.

   How many butterflies were there in all? $10 + 4 = 14$

   How many butterflies were left? $10 - 4 = 6$

3. **5** caterpillars were on a hill.
   2 caterpillars were on the ground.

   How many caterpillars were there in all? $5 + 2 = 7$

   How many caterpillars were left? $5 - 2 = 3$

4. **8** flies landed on a fruit basket.
   7 flies flew away.

   How many flies were there in all? $8 + 7 = 15$

   How many flies were left? $8 - 7 = 1$

6 bees were on a flower.
3 bees flew away.
How many bees were **left**?

Solve

$$\begin{array}{r} 6 \\ - 3 \\ \hline 3 \end{array}$$ bees

---

1. **5** bees were at the hive.
3 bees flew away.
How many bees
were **left**?

Solve

_____
○ _____
_____ bees

---

2. **6** bears were in the woods.
4 bears went away.
How many bears
were **left**?

Solve

_____
○ _____
_____ bears

---

3. Bear had **6** jars of honey.
He gave away **2** jars.
How many jars of honey
did he have **left**?

Solve

_____
○ _____
_____ jars

ON THE FARM

11 goats are in the pen.
5 goats are outside the pen.
How many goats are there **altogether**?

Solve

$$
\begin{array}{r}
11 \\
+\ 5 \\
\hline
16
\end{array}
\text{ goats}
$$

1. **7** sheep are in the pen.
   5 sheep are in the yard.
   How many **more** sheep are in the pen than in the yard?

Solve

_____ sheep

2. **8** cows are white.
   5 cows are brown.
   How many cows are there **in all**?

Solve

_____ cows

3. There were **12** eggs in the nest.
   4 eggs hatched.
   How many eggs were **left**?

Solve

_____ eggs

Karla had **25** seeds.
She planted **15** seeds.
How many seeds did she have **left**?

Solve

$$\begin{array}{r} 25 \\ (-)\ 15 \\ \hline 10 \end{array} \text{ seeds}$$

Sweet Peas

1. Miguel saw **34** robins.
   13 robins flew away.
   How many robins were **left**?

Solve

◯ _____ / _____

_____ robins

2. Craig saw **13** tulips in the park.
   He saw **11** more tulips at home.
   How many tulips were there **in all**?

Solve

◯ _____ / _____

_____ tulips

3. Sarah saw **23** butterflies.
   She saw **14** more butterflies later.
   How many butterflies did she see **altogether**?

Solve

◯ _____ / _____

_____ butterflies

Eric saw **11** beach balls.
Then he saw **3** more beach balls.
How many beach balls did he see **altogether**?

Solve

$$
\begin{array}{r}
11 \\
+\ \ 3 \\
\hline
14
\end{array}
$$
beach balls

---

1. Mandy took **13** pictures.
   Then she took **6** more pictures.
   How many pictures did she take
   in all?

   Solve

   _____ pictures

---

2. Alyssa caught **15** fish.
   8 fish got away.
   How many fish does she have **left**?

   Solve

   _____ fish

---

3. Brian bought **14** postcards.
   He mailed **7** of them.
   How many postcards does he have **left**?

   Solve

   _____ postcards

FALL FUN

There were **7** people on the hay wagon.
5 more people got on.
How many people were on the
hay wagon **altogether**?

Solve

$$\begin{array}{r} 7 \\ +\ 5 \\ \hline 12 \end{array}$$ people

---

I. There were **6** piles of leaves.
Claire put **4** piles of leaves into bags.
How many piles of leaves were **left** to bag?

Solve

$\bigcirc$ _____

_____ piles of
leaves

---

2. There were **8** home games.
There were **10** away games.
What was the **total** number of football games?

Solve

$\bigcirc$ _____

_____ games

---

3. There were **16** apples on
the tree.
Shawn picked **4** of them.
How many apples were
left on the tree?

Solve

$\bigcirc$ _____

_____ apples

Circle the correct question and number sentence for each word problem.

1. **10** ladybugs were in the garden.
   5 ladybugs left the garden.

How many ladybugs were there in all? $5 + 5 = 10$

How many ladybugs were left? $10 - 5 = 5$

---

2. **11** beetles were on a log.
   3 more beetles came along.

How many beetles are there in all? $11 + 3 = 14$

How many beetles were left? $11 - 3 = 8$

---

3. **8** ants were on a watermelon.
   7 more ants were on the ground.

How many ants were there in all? $8 + 7 = 15$

How many ants were left? $8 - 7 = 1$

---

4. **12** bees were at a hive.
   3 bees flew away.

How many bees were there in all? $12 + 3 = 15$

How many bees were left? $12 - 3 = 9$

Use the picture graph to answer the questions.

Name	Number of Books Read
Ann	📖 📖 📖 📖 📖 📖
Bret	📖 📖 📖 📖 📖 📖 📖 📖 📖
Chan	📖 📖 📖 📖 📖
Zach	📖 📖 📖 📖
Emma	📖 📖 📖 📖 📖 📖 📖 📖

1. How many books did Ann read? _____

2. How many books did Chan read? _____

3. How many books did Emma read? _____

4. Who read the most books? _____

5. Who read the fewest books? _____

6. How many books did Bret and Zach read **altogether**?

   _____ ◯ _____ = _____

7. How many books did Ann and Chan read **in all**?

   _____ ◯ _____ = _____

8. Emma read **more** books than Ann. How many **more** books did Emma read?

   _____ ◯ _____ = _____

Use the picture graph to answer the questions.

Name	Number of Baseballs
Sam	⚾ ⚾ ⚾ ⚾
Dana	⚾ ⚾ ⚾ ⚾ ⚾
Beth	⚾ ⚾ ⚾
Tom	⚾ ⚾
Jim	⚾ ⚾ ⚾ ⚾ ⚾ ⚾
Heidi	⚾ ⚾ ⚾ ⚾ ⚾

1. How many baseballs does Sam have? _____

2. How many baseballs does Dana have? _____

3. How many baseballs does Beth have? _____

4. How many baseballs does Tom have? _____

5. How many baseballs does Jim have? _____

6. How many baseballs does Heidi have? _____

7. How many baseballs do Beth and Dana have **altogether**?

    _____ ◯ _____ = _____

8. Jim has **more** baseballs than Sam.
    How many **more** baseballs does Jim have?

    _____ ◯ _____ = _____

Use the bar graph to answer the questions.

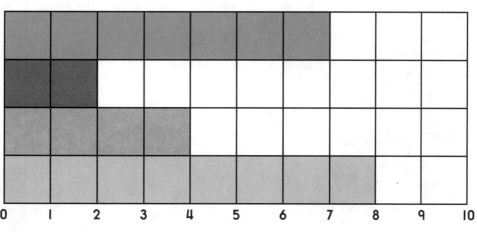

Boxes of Cookies Sold

1. How many boxes of cookies did Kay sell? _____

2. How many boxes of cookies did Tim sell? _____

3. How many boxes of cookies did Tim and Jeff sell **in all**?

   _____ ◯ _____ = _____

4. How many boxes of cookies did Chris and Jeff sell **altogether**?

   _____ ◯ _____ = _____

5. Chris sold **more** boxes of cookies than Tim. How many **more** boxes of cookies did Chris sell?

   _____ ◯ _____ = _____

6. How many boxes of cookies did Tim and Kay sell **in all**?

   _____ ◯ _____ = _____

Use the bar graph to answer the questions.

1. How many marbles does Joe have? _____

2. How many marbles does Mike have? _____

3. How many marbles does Cindy have? _____

4. Cindy has **more** marbles than Joe.
   How many **more** marbles does Cindy have?

5. Mike has **more** marbles than Joe.
   How many **more** marbles does Mike have?

6. How many marbles do Joe and Cindy
   have **altogether**?

FAVORITE PETS

Use the tally table to answer the questions.

Pet		Number of Votes
Bird		////
Cat		//// ////
Dog		//// //// //
Fish		//// /
Pony		///

/ = 1 vote
//// = 5 votes

1. How many votes did the pony get? _____

2. How many votes did the bird get? _____

3. How many votes did the fish get? _____

4. Which animal got the most votes? _____

5. Which animal got the fewest votes? _____

6. The cat got **more** votes than the fish.
   How many **more** votes did the cat get?

   _____ ◯ _____ = _____

7. How many votes did the bird and the fish get **in all**?

   _____ ◯ _____ = _____

FREE THROWS

Use the table to answer the questions.

Name	Points
Michael	30
Laura	46
Kayla	28
Jamal	33
Bradley	40

1. How many points does Kayla have? _____

2. How many points does Michael have? _____

3. Who has the most points? _____

4. Who has the fewest points? _____

5. Who has more points than Jamal?

_____ and _____

6. Who has fewer points than Jamal?

_____ and _____

7. How many points do Jamal and Michael have **in all**? _____ ◯ _____

8. Bradley has **more** points than Kayla. How many **more** points does Bradley have? _____ ◯ _____

DAYS AND DATES

1. Write the missing numbers in the calendar.

June

Sunday	Monday	Tuesday	Wednesday	Thursday	Friday	Saturday
		1	2		4	5
6		8		10		12
13	14		16		18	
20		22		24		26
	28		30			

2. What day comes after Tuesday? _____

3. What day comes before Friday? _____

4. What day of the week is June 15? _____

5. What is the date of the first Monday? _____

6. What is the date of the second Friday? _____

7. How many days are in one week? _____

8. How many days are in two weeks? _____ ◯ _____ = _____

9. How many days are in June? _____

DATES AND DAYS

1. Write the missing numbers in the calendar.

December						
Sunday	Monday	Tuesday	Wednesday	Thursday	Friday	Saturday
				1		3
4		6	7		9	
11	12			15		17
	19		21		23	
25		27			30	31

2. What day comes after Friday? _____

3. What day of the week is December 21? _____

4. What is the date of the second Wednesday? _____

5. What is the date of the third Monday? _____

6. How many days are in three weeks? ____ ◯ ____ ◯ ____ = ____

7. How many days are in December? _____

8. What date is two weeks after December 6? _____

9. What date is one week before December 25? _____

Read and solve each word problem.

Jenna played the piano for **20** minutes.
She read a book for **15** minutes.
How many minutes did she spend
playing and reading?

Solve

$$\begin{array}{r} 20 \\ (+)\ 15 \\ \hline 35 \end{array}$$ minutes

---

1. Ken read a book for **45** minutes.
   He played soccer for **30** minutes.
   How many more minutes did he
   spend reading?

Solve

_____
○ _____
_____ minutes

---

2. Nathan studied for **25** minutes.
   He played a game for **10** minutes.
   How many more minutes did he
   spend studying?

Solve

_____
○ _____
_____ minutes

---

3. Lani walked her dog for **30** minutes.
   She washed her dog for **15** minutes.
   How many minutes did she spend
   with her dog?

Solve

_____
○ _____
_____ minutes

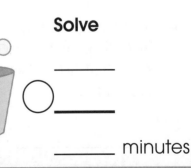

Read and solve each word problem.
Draw hands on the clocks to show the
starting time and ending time of each activity.

Start **End**

The movie starts at **5:00**.
It is **2** hours long. At what
time does the movie end?

__7:00__

---

1. The game starts at **1:30**.
   It is **3** hours long. At what
   time does the game end?

   Start **End**

   ____:____

---

2. The concert ended at **4:00**.
   It was **2** hours long. At what
   time did the concert start?

   Start **End**

   ____:____

---

3. School starts at **8:30**.
   It ends **7** hours later.
   At what time does
   the school day end?

   Start **End**

   ____:____

---

4. Rachel woke up at **7:00**.
   She slept for **10** hours.
   At what time did she
   go to bed?

   Start **End**

   ____:____

Read and solve each word problem.
Draw hands on the clocks to show the
starting time and ending time of each activity.

Start   **End**

Brett starts to eat at **5:30**.
He eats for **30** minutes. At what
time does he finish eating?

_____6:00_____

---

1. Heather starts to read at **3:00**.
She reads for **20** minutes. At what
time does she stop reading?

Start   **End**

_____ : _____

---

2. The play ended at **7:45**.
It was **40** minutes long. At
what time did the play start?

Start   **End**

_____ : _____

---

3. Music lessons started at **4:30**.
Parker's lesson was **30** minutes
long. At what time did his
music lesson end?

Start   **End**

_____ : _____

---

4. Stephanie put a cake in the oven
at **10:30**. It baked for **45** minutes.
At what time did the cake come
out of the oven?

Start   **End**

_____ : _____

Jane has **8** balloons.
~~Jake has **4** balloons.~~
Brandon has **9** balloons.
How many balloons do
Jane and Brandon have?

Solve

$$\begin{array}{r} 8 \\ +\ 9 \\ \hline 17 \end{array}$$ balloons

---

Read each word problem. Cross out the
information you do not need. Then solve
each word problem.

1. Emily is **12** years old.
   Her brother is **5** years old.
   Her sister is **8** years old.
   How much older than her
   brother is Emily?

Solve

○ _____
   _____

_____ years

---

2. Alex bought **7** gifts.
   Randy bought **8** gifts.
   Ashley bought **5** gifts.
   How many gifts did Randy
   and Ashley buy?

Solve

○ _____
   _____

_____ gifts

---

3. Mark has **10** pizza slices.
   Jada has **7** pizza slices.
   Jose has **9** pizza slices.
   Brittany has **5** pizza slices.
   How many more pizza slices
   than Brittany does Jada have?

Solve

○ _____
   _____

_____ pizza
   slices

GROWTH FACTOR

Drew is **45** inches tall.
~~His father is **69** inches tall.~~
His mother is **63** inches tall.
How much taller than Drew
is his mother?

Solve

$$\begin{array}{r} 63 \\ \ominus\ \underline{45} \\ \underline{18} \end{array}$$ inches

---

Read each word problem. Cross out the
information you do not need. Then solve
each word problem.

1. Taylor weighs **67** pounds.
   Cory weighs **72** pounds.
   Mitchell weighs **65** pounds.
   How much do Cory and
   Mitchell weigh in all?

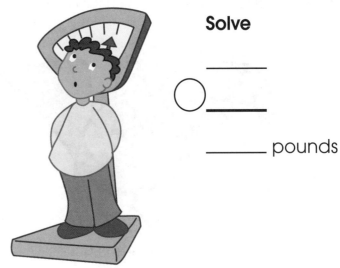

Solve

_____
◯ _____

_____ pounds

---

2. Ellie's father is **35** years old.
   Her uncle is **39** years old.
   Her grandmother is **30** years older than her uncle.
   Ellie is **8** years old.
   How old is Ellie's grandmother?

Solve

_____
◯ _____

_____ years
old

Help these math birds return to their answer nests!
Write their names in the correct nests.

Al

The number is 2 greater than 10 + 3.

Bob

The number is 1 less than 2 tens + 8 ones.

Joe

The number is 4 less than 4 + 0.

Ben

The number is an even number between 14 and 20.

Sue

The number is 5 less than 9 + 9.

1. 16
_____

2. 13
_____

3. 27
_____

4. 15
_____

5. 0
_____

ANSWER KEY

Page 1

Page 2

Page 3

Toys	Animals
ball	cat
top	cow
doll	dog

Page 4

Page 8

Page 5

Page 6

Page 7

Page 9

Page 10
1. swan
2. zebra
3. bobcat
4. ostrich

Page 11
1. dog
2. cat
3. fish
4. bird

Page 12
1. hat
2. bat
3. fan
4. pan
5. had, mad, sad
6. man, ran, can

Page 13
1. at, as, am, an
2. cat, fan, ant, had
3. bat, hat, mat, pat
4. ham, jam, Sam, ram
5. ran, man, pan, fan

Page 14

1. net, pet, jet
2. hen, men, ten

Page 15
1. sled
2. bell
3. red
4. ten
5. bed
6. nest

Page 16
1. out, in
2. hers, his
3. big, pig
   dig, wig

Page 17
1. I hid a lid, I did.
2. I will fill a hill with flowers.
3. The big pig ate a fig.
4. I wish the fish were still on the dish.
5. hid, lid, did
6. will, fill, hill
7. big, pig, fig
8. wish, fish, dish

Page 18
1. fox
2. doll
3. hot, not, tot
4. box

Page 19
1. clock
2. lock
3. sock
4. box
5. dock
6. rock

Page 20
1. pup
2. gum
3. fun
4. hug
5. bug
6. cup
7. sun
8. mud

Page 21

short a
cat
man
short e
hen
red
short i
pig
big

short o
top
hop
short u
sun
bus

Page 22

```
h   s o c k
a   u
t e n
    g
p i g
```

Page 23

```
Q W R T U P B F D
O D B M L J D M O
W O X D P W D J L
R G Q A B S R Z L
P T W Y S H U K P
M D U C K X M X J
G Q W M N F R P K
S Y G D J D A D B
B D I S H H K C F
```

Page 24

```
E H O R N G F L H
P K S N X Q P X A
H G C H O O K N T
A B K Z M Q R T Q
M J H E A R T V K
W Z W P R T B K C
K R Q D Q K N H M
P H O U S E R E T
Z T P J N K B N Q
```

Page 25

1. vase
2. cake
3. tape
4. rake
5. game, gate

Page 26

```
          t
          r
          e
      s e e d
  c       r
  l e a v e      k
  e       a      e
  a     m o n e y
b e a n
```

Page 27

1. seal
2. tree
3. leaf
4. bee
5. me, he

Page 28

1. kite
2. bike
3. tie
4. ride
5. fine
6. like

Page 29

1. kind, find
2. night, right
3. cry, try
4. My friend and <u>I</u> took a <u>hike</u> up a hill.
   We flew our <u>kites</u> <u>high</u> in the <u>sky</u>.
   My friend and <u>I</u> had a fun <u>time</u>.

Page 30

1. note
2. boat
3. told
4. grow
5. show
6. goat
7. home
8. hold

Page 31

1. grow
2. coat
3. slow
4. bow
5. own
6. goat
7. told
   a rowboat

Page 32

1. cute
2. tube
3. huge
4. rule
5. mule
6. cube

Page 33

1. clue
2. true
3. cute
4. huge
5. blue
6. use

Page 34

```
r a k e      b
    i        e
  t u b e
  e   o
      n
s l i d e
```

Page 35

1. cake, baby
2. bee, tree
3. kite, tie
4. boat, rope
5. tube, blue

Page 36

Page 37

1. mane 2. kite 3. pine 4. huge 5. dime 6. made
7. huge
8. made
9. dime
10. kite
11. pine
12. mane

Page 38

```
Q D L P J S I T V
W S F M B X Y O H
Q I J K S S T A R
C N V U N W L X M
S G P M A K J B R
E Z S Q I J S U N
A Q M P L C Q P K
L S O A P I P G K
E P F T W S O C K
```

Page 39

```
R A I N F T Y P Q
R B S Q O W R U R
I K B J P Q O K O
N H R E D Z B R S
G K L O L J O Q I
R O S E R W T P N
V R Z Q O W Z J L
Z U I F P R H N Q
I G C Q E W F C W
```

Page 40

1. shop
2. shoe
3. show
4. shirt
5. shell
6. push
7. dish
8. wash
9. wish

ANSWER KEY

Page 41

Page 42

1. bath
2. think
3. path
4. thirty
5. Thank, there

Page 43

1. whale
2. white
3. inch
4. path
5. she
6. branch
   winter

Page 44

Roy was in a toy store with his mother. He had save his coins to buy a new toy. There were many kinds of toys. Some toys made too much noise. Some toys cost too much. He finally made a choice. Roy counted all his coins. He chose a toy he could enjoy with his friends.

1. in a toy store
2. his mother
3. **oi**   **oy**
   coins   Roy
   noise   toy
   choice   enjoy
   Answers will vary.

Page 45

Mom and I saw a brown mouse in our house. Our cat saw it and gave a howl. He jumped down onto the floor and started to run. The cat chased the mouse around the house. We opened the door to let the mouse out. It let out a squeak, and away it ran.

1. Mom and I
2. house, mouse
3. **ou**   **ow**
   mouse   brown
   our   howl
   house   down
   Answers will vary.

Page 48

1. cat   2. city
   cow   circus
   cup   cent
3. gas   4. general
   gum   gentle
   good   giraffe

Page 46

1. stool
2. school
3. blue
4. glue
5. few
6. new

Page 49

1. The king began to sing.
2. Her cat wears a hat.
3. The dog ran after the frog.
4. I wish I had a fish.
5. My coat is in the boat.
6. A vet took care of my pet.

Page 50

1. The pail fell in the well.
2. Look at my new book.
3. The boy had a new toy.
4. I like your new bike.
5. I was told you had a cold.
6. The pig wore a wig.

Page 47

1. tool
2. new
3. food
4. soon
5. blue
6. moon
7. zoo
8. flew
9. stew   10. mood
11. cool   12. room
13. blew   14. knew

Page 51

Page 52

1. hot
2. dog
3. sock
4. fox
5. clock

Page 53

1. bed
2. fish
3. lake
4. coat
5. bell

Page 54

1. bike
2. dime
3. kite
4. night
5. pie
6. cry

Page 55

1. moon
2. honey
3. mouse
4. cow
5. boat
6. book

Page 56

1. spring
2. round
3. day

Page 57

1. white
2. running
3. snow
4. showers

Page 58 / Page 59

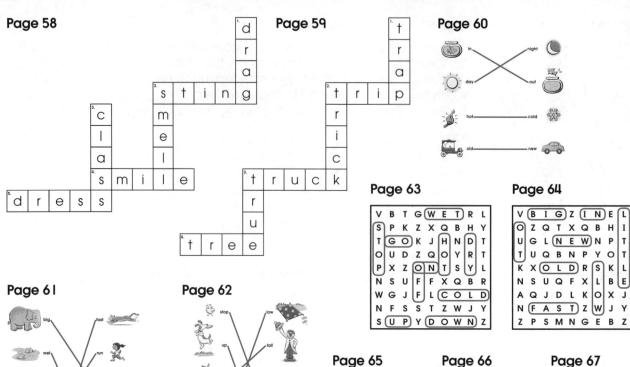

Crossword puzzles (Pages 58–59):
- drape / sting / smell / camel / class / smile / dress / tree
- train / trip / trick / truck / tru

Page 60

Matching:
- in — out
- day — night
- hot — cold
- old — new

Page 63

V	B	T	G	W	E	T	R	L
S	P	K	Z	X	Q	B	H	Y
T	G	O	K	J	H	N	D	T
O	U	D	Z	Q	O	Y	R	Y
P	X	Z	O	N	T	S	Y	L
N	S	U	F	F	X	Q	B	R
W	G	J	F	L	C	O	L	D
N	F	S	S	T	Z	W	J	Y
S	U	P	Y	D	O	W	N	Z

Page 64

V	B	I	G	Z	I	N	E	L
O	Z	Q	T	X	Q	B	H	I
U	G	L	N	E	W	N	P	T
T	U	Q	B	N	P	Y	O	L
K	X	O	L	D	R	S	K	E
N	S	U	Q	F	X	L	L	Y
A	Q	J	D	L	K	O	X	J
N	F	A	S	T	Z	W	W	J
Z	P	S	M	N	G	E	B	Z

Page 65
1. rainbow
2. cupcake
3. birdhouse
4. football
5. butterfly
6. baseball

Page 66
1. doghouse
2. firefly
3. basketball
4. starfish
5. rattlesnake
6. sunflower
7. skateboard

Page 67
1. don't
2. isn't
3. haven't
4. Let's
5. shouldn't
6. we'll

Page 61

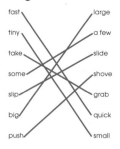

Matching: big / fast / wet / run / on / little / walk / off / slow / dry

Page 62

Matching: stop / low / up / tall / short / under / high / go / over / down

Page 68
1. doesn't
2. isn't
3. they're
4. she's
5. can't
6. aren't
7. I'm
8. we're
9. don't
10. couldn't
11. he'd
12. we'll
13. wouldn't
14. it's

Page 69
Matching: fast — large / tiny — a few / take — slide / some — shove / slip — grab / big — quick / push — small

Page 70
Matching: give — slow / after — small / large — before / old — none / fast — take / all — new / hot — over / under — cold

Page 71
1. to
2. there
3. hear
4. won
5. right
6. ate

Page 72

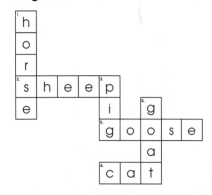

Crossword: horse / sheep / pig / goose / goat / cat

Page 73
1. yes
2. yes
3. no
4. yes
5. no
6. no

Page 74
1. yes
2. no
3. yes
4. no
5. no
6. yes

Page 75
1. dogs
2. ducks
3. chickens
4. frogs
5. birds

Page 76
Liz, Henry
Chan, Beth

Page 77
Ken
Mia, Ty
Mimi, Sarah

Page 78
Zeke
Jill, Peter
Adam, Jessie

ANSWER KEY

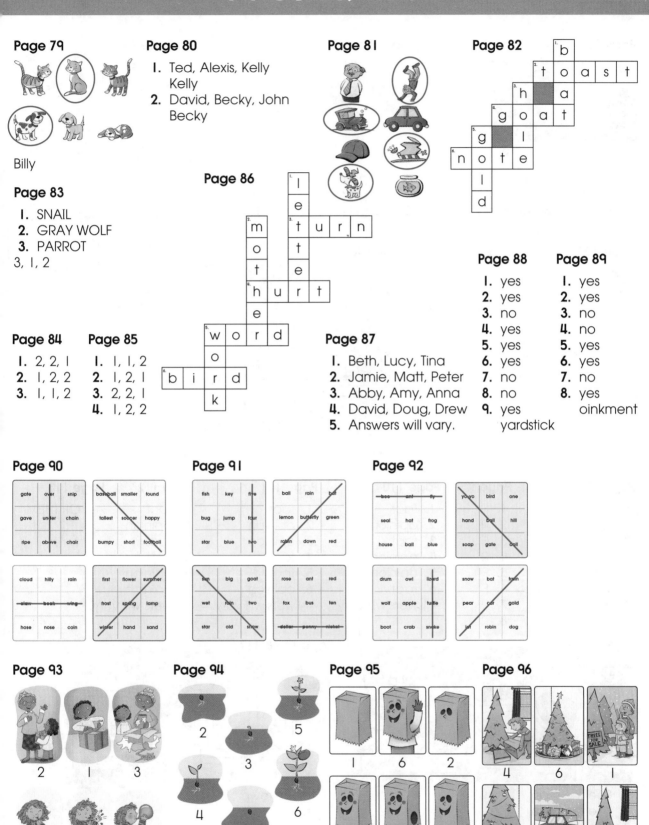

Page 79

Billy

Page 80

1. Ted, Alexis, Kelly
   Kelly
2. David, Becky, John
   Becky

Page 81

Page 82

Page 83

1. SNAIL
2. GRAY WOLF
3. PARROT

3, 1, 2

Page 86

Page 84

1. 2, 2, 1
2. 1, 2, 2
3. 1, 1, 2

Page 85

1. 1, 1, 2
2. 1, 2, 1
3. 2, 2, 1
4. 1, 2, 2

Page 87

1. Beth, Lucy, Tina
2. Jamie, Matt, Peter
3. Abby, Amy, Anna
4. David, Doug, Drew
5. Answers will vary.

Page 88

1. yes
2. yes
3. no
4. yes
5. yes
6. yes
7. no
8. no
9. yes
   yardstick

Page 89

1. yes
2. yes
3. no
4. no
5. yes
6. yes
7. no
8. yes
   oinkment

Page 90

Page 91

Page 92

Page 93

Page 94

Page 95

Page 96

ANSWER KEY

Page 97

2 1 3

1. The girl bought a ticket.
2. The girl flew in an airplane.
3. The girl saw her grandparents.

Page 98

2 3 1

1. The girl carried her sled up the hill.
2. The girl rode her sled down the hill.
3. The girl fell off her sled.

Page 99

2 3 1

1 3 2

3 2 1

Page 100

2 3 1

1 2 3

1 3 2

Page 101

1. seed
2. tree
3. blossoms
4. fruit
5. seeds

Page 102

4 dogs

Page 103

2
5
1
4
3

Page 104

2
3
1
4

Page 105

3
1
4
5
2

Page 106

Answers will vary.

Page 107

Answers will vary.

Page 108

1. make-believe
   real
2. real
   make-believe
3. real
   make-believe
4. make-believe
   real

Page 109

1. F
2. R
3. F
4. R
5. F
6. F
7. R
8. R

Page 110

1. fact
2. opinion
3. fact
4. opinion
5. opinion
6. fact

Answers will vary.

Page 111

1. fact
2. opinion
3. opinion
4. fact
5. fact
6. opinion

Answers will vary.

Page 112

1. fact
2. opinion
3. fact
4. fact
5. opinion
6. opinion

Answers will vary.

Page 113

ALL OF THEM

Page 114 & 115

1. See the map.
2. See the map.
3. See the map.
4. Answers will vary.
5. yes
6. yes
7. no

Page 116 & 117

1. ghost town
2. no
3. yes
4. coyote
5. pond
6. See the map.
7. Answers will vary.

Page 118

Page 123

Page 119
1. east
2. southeast
3. northwest
4. southwest

Page 120
1. Billy
2. Dad
3. farmer
4. cows
5. dog
6. chicken

Page 124

people	animals
family	cows
neighbor	Hens
uncle	horse
brother	chickens
places	**things**
farm	eggs
barn	fence
field	tractor

Page 121
1. horse
2. pig
3. goat
4. cow
5. duck
6. dog

Page 125
1. dogs
2. names
3. spots
4. ears
5. balls
6. bones

Page 122

places	things
zoo	pizza
house	book
town	bike

Answers will vary.

Page 126

1. Polly
2. Puff
3. Peter
4. Bubbles
5. Duke

Page 127
1. Tuesday   2. Thursday
3. Monday   4. Saturday

Page 131

Five ducks <u>waddle</u> to the pond.
They <u>jump</u> into the cool water.
They <u>paddle</u> with their feet.
They <u>dive</u> under the water.
They <u>bob</u> back up.
They <u>swim</u> to the other side.
Then they <u>fly</u> away.
1. waddle
2. jump
3. swim
4. fly

Page 132

A ladybug is a <u>small</u> beetle.
It has a <u>round</u> body.
It may have <u>red</u> or <u>orange</u> wings.
The wings have <u>black</u> spots.
This <u>tiny</u> insect helps people.
Ladybugs eat <u>harmful</u> insects.
1. beetle
2. wings
3. body
4. insects

Page 128
1. play
2. hits
3. flies
4. runs
5. catch
6. drop

Page 133
1. hot
2. loud
3. cold
4. soft
5. wet
6. quiet

Page 134
1. rainy
2. windy
3. cloudy
4. snowy

Page 129

Page 130
1. plants
2. grows
3. pulls
4. waters
5. eats
6. digs

Page 135
1. Lady is a <u>big</u> cat.
2. She had <u>three</u> kittens.
3. Tiger is the <u>striped</u> kitten.
4. Jet is the <u>black</u> kitten.
5. The <u>little</u> kitten is Socks.
6. We now have <u>four</u> cats.

Page 136

1. <u>Our family</u> visited Yellowstone National Park. — who
2. <u>The park</u> has lakes and springs. — what
3. <u>People</u> camp in the park. — who
4. <u>Stars</u> fill the night sky. — what
5. <u>Forests</u> are everywhere. — what
6. <u>Hikers</u> climb hills. — who
7. Answers will vary.
8. Answers will vary.

Page 137

1. Dani <u>brings milk</u>.
2. Josh <u>grabs bananas</u>.
3. Kim <u>takes a salad</u>.
4. Billy <u>carries hot dogs</u>.
5. They all <u>eat together</u>.
Answers will vary.

Page 138

1. Owls <u>hunt at night</u>.
2. Elk <u>eat green plants</u>.
3. Eagles <u>nest in the park</u>.
4. Water <u>shoots up from underground</u>.
5. Hikers <u>walk down trails</u>.
6. The forest <u>is quiet</u>.
7. Answers will vary.
8. Answers will vary.

Page 139

1. <u>I love fruit</u>, so I packed a (banana)/pizza for lunch.
2. A feather <u>tickled my nose</u>, so I (sneezed)/cried.
3. The snow was pretty/(heavy). <u>It broke the tree limb</u>.
4. <u>It was my birthday</u>, so we had a circus/(party).
5. <u>He gave his mom a rose</u>. She (smiled)/frowned and said, "Thank you."

Page 140

1. who
2. where
3. when
4. why
Answers will vary.

Page 141

1. <u>o</u>ur dog is hungry.
2. <u>d</u>ad brings food.
3. <u>s</u>kip eats quickly.
4. <u>f</u>ood goes on the floor.
5. <u>d</u>ogs are messy.
6. <u>n</u>ow I need to clean up.
Answers will vary.

Page 142

1. <u>is</u> mother home?
2. <u>where</u> did she go?
3. <u>when</u> will she be back?
4. <u>who</u> baked the cookies?
5. <u>they</u> are good.
6. <u>may i</u> have another one?
Answers will vary.

Page 143

1. My team played soccer today.
2. The most amazing thing happened!
3. The score was 3 to 3.
4. Our team got the ball!
5. We made a goal!
6. It was awesome!
Answers will vary.

Page 144

1. Answers will vary.

Page 145

1. Answers will vary.
2. Answers will vary.

Page 146

1. Answers will vary.
2. Answers will vary.

Page 147

1. The baby is given dinner.
2. The family looks for it.
3. The family packs up and leaves.
4. The tire is fixed.
5. Bill puts on a new shirt.

Page 148

Page 149

Page 150

Cause — Effect

1. The glass could break.
2. You could get burned.
3. Seeing something funny.

Page 151

2
3
4
1

Page 152

1. Sid's Shapes
2. circle
3. no
4. yes
5. 6. △

Page 153

1. bus
2. Sue
3. kids
4. no
5. yes
6. school
7. 7 or seven

Page 154

10

1. Ben's Hen
2. Ben has a pet hen.

Page 155

1. Anna was in a bike race.
2. 5
Answers will vary.

ANSWER KEY

Page 156
1. F
2. T
3. T
4. F
Answers will vary.

Page 157
1. Answers will vary.
2. Play Day
Answers will vary.

Page 158
1. walking to school
2. The car splashed water on him.
Answers will vary.

Page 159
1. shopping for shoes
2. her purse
3. Her purse had been found.
Answers will vary.

Page 160
1. an invitation
2. 4th of July party or picnic
3. 6:00
4. He should bring the food he likes to eat.
5. They will have a picnic and watch fireworks.

Page 161
1. a sign
2. in the park
3. 10:00 and 2:00
Answers will vary.

Page 162
1. the library
2. pick out a book
3. bring it back
Answers will vary.

Page 163
1. who wrote the book the title of the book
2. Joan Hoffman
3. Reading Made Easy
4. The book is about reading.

Page 164
1. T
2. T
3. T
4. F

Page 165
1. Snails creep along on a foot.
2. Snails live in shady places.
3. Snails eat rotting plants.
4. Snails lay their eggs in the ground.

Page 166
1. Erica wrote the note.
2. Adam is with Erica.
3. They are going to the park.
4. They will be home by noon.

Page 167
1. a poem
2. dance
3. starting to grow
4. walk — shower
5. May — talk
6. flower — say
7. wish — fish

Pages 168 & 169
1. zoo
2. Answers will vary.
3. Answers will vary.
4. at school
5. Answers will vary.
6. a classroom
7. Answers will vary.

Page 170

summer: shorts, flip-flops, beach, t-shirts
both: friends
winter: coat, boots, hat

Page 171
1. 2 + 2 = 4
2. 3 + 3 = 6
3. 4 + 2 = 6
4. 1 + 3 = 4
5. 1 + 1 = 2
6. 5 + 1 = 6
7. 2 + 3 = 5

Page 172
1. 3 + 4 = 7
2. 5 + 2 = 7
3. 1 + 6 = 7
4. 5 + 3 = 8
5. 7 + 1 = 8
6. 2 + 6 = 8
7. 4 + 4 = 8

Page 173
1. 11   2. 12   3. 10
4. 11   5. 9   6. 9
7. 11   8. 9   9. 10
10. 12   11. 10   12. 11   13. 12
14. 12   15. 10   16. 9   17. 10
18. 10   19. 12   20. 9   21. 11

Page 174
1. 11   2. 12   3. 12   4. 11
5. 12   6. 10   7. 11   8. 12
9. 10   10. 12   11. 10   12. 11

Page 175

Page 176

Page 177
1. 2
   +6
   ───
   8 birds
2. 1
   +5
   ───
   6 turtles
3. 4
   +3
   ───
   7 dogs

Page 178
1. 5   2. 7
3. 9   4. 3
5. 6   6. 10
7. 8   8. 4

Page 179

ANSWER KEY

Page 180
1. 3,④
2. ⑥,4
3. 5,⑥
4. 3,⑤
5. ⑦,6
6. ③,2

Page 181

7. Draw a group of ❀ to show 1 fewer than is.

🦋🦋🦋🦋🦋🦋🦋🦋 How many ❀ are there? 9

Page 182
1. 5,③
2. ④,6
3. ⑥,7
4. 9,⑦
5. 10,⑧
6. 6,⑤

Page 183
1. 2
2. 3
3. 4
4. 5
5. 3
6. 4
7. 5
8. 5

Page 184
1. 3
2. 5
3. 5
4. 4
5. 5
6. 2
7. 4
8. 5

Page 185
1. 2
2. 3
3. 2
4. 1
5. 1
6. 2
7. 1
8. 1

Page 186
1. 4 − 3 = 1
2. 6 − 3 = 3
3. 2 − 1 = 1
4. 5 − 2 = 3
5. 5 − 4 = 1
6. 6 − 4 = 2
7. 6 − 1 = 5

Page 187
1. 7 − 5 = 2
2. 7 − 4 = 3
3. 7 − 1 = 6
4. 8 − 3 = 5
5. 8 − 5 = 3
6. 8 − 2 = 6
7. 8 − 7 = 1

Page 188
1. 9 − 4 = 5
2. 9 − 2 = 7
3. 9 − 6 = 3
4. 10 − 8 = 2
5. 10 − 4 = 6
6. 10 − 7 = 3
7. 10 − 5 = 5

Page 189

5. 3 6. 5 7. 6
8. 2 9. 4 10. 7

Page 190
1. 8 −4 = 4 kayaks
2. 6 −3 = 3 powerboats
3. 8 −2 = 6 surfboards

Page 191
1. 5 −4 = 1 fish
2. 8 −4 = 4 flowers
3. 7 −5 = 2 turtles

Page 192
1. 4
2. 3
3. 2
4. 2
5. 2
6. 1
7. 1
8. 3

Page 193

+	0	1	2	3	4	5
0	0	1	2	3	4	5
1	1	2	3	4	5	
2	2	3	4	5		
3	3	4	5			
4	4	5				
5	5					

Page 194
1. 4 2. 2 3. 2
4. 4 5. 5 6. 1
7. 2 8. 3 9. 5
10. 4 11. 1 12. 5 13. 3
14. 1 15. 3 16. 4 17. 3

Page 195
1. 7
2. 8
3. 9
4. 6
5. 10
6. 7
7. 10
8. 9

Page 196
1. 7 2. 7
   9   9
   8   10
   10   8
3. 8 4. 9
   9   7
   7   8
   10   10

Page 197

+	0	1	2	3	4	5	6	7	8	9
0	0	1	2	3	4	5	6	7	8	9
1	1	2	3	4	5	6	7	8	9	10
2	2	3	4	5	6	7	8	9	10	
3	3	4	5	6	7	8	9	10		
4	4	5	6	7	8	9	10			
5	5	6	7	8	9	10				
6	6	7	8	9	10					
7	7	8	9	10						
8	8	9	10							
9	9	10								

Each sum is 10.

ANSWER KEY

Page 198
1. 9, 9   2. 7, 7   3. 10, 10
4. 10, 10   5. 8, 8   6. 8, 8

7. 9, 5 + 4 = 9   8. 7, 4 + 3 = 7
9. 6, 0 + 6 = 6   10. 10, 2 + 8 = 10
11. 9, 9 + 0 = 9   12. 8, 7 + 1 = 8

13. 2 + 7 = 9, 7 + 2 = 9
14. 4 + 6 = 10, 6 + 4 = 10
15. 0 + 8 = 8, 8 + 0 = 8

Page 199
1. 5   2. 5   3. 6
4. 8   5. 6   6. 4
7. 2   8. 6   9. 0   10. 5
11. 7   12. 3   13. 2   14. 2
15. 8 − 5 = 3

Page 200
1. 4, 3   2. 4, 5   3. 7, 0
4. 8, 1   5. 8, 2   6. 2, 6

7. 4, 9 − 4 = 5   8. 2, 7 − 2 = 5
9. 6, 6 − 6 = 0   10. 8, 10 − 8 = 2
11. 0, 8 − 0 = 8   12. 7, 8 − 7 = 1

13. 9 − 3 = 6, 9 − 6 = 3
14. 10 − 2 = 8, 10 − 8 = 2
15. 9 − 0 = 9, 9 − 9 = 0

Page 201

Page 202
1. 9   2. 5   3. 9
4. 9   5. 9   6. 5
7. 8   8. 9   9. 10
10. 10   11. 4   12. 7   13. 7
14. 3   15. 10   16. 10   17. 6

Page 203
1. 10 and 5, 15
2. 10 and 7, 17
3. 10 and 10, 20
4. 10 and 3, 13
5. 10 and 6, 16
6. 10 and 1, 11

Page 204
1. 11, 12, 13, 14, 15, 16, 17, 18, 19, 20
2. 11, 12, 13, 14, 15, 16, 17, 18, 19
3. 5, 6, 7, 8, 9, 10, 11, 12, 13, 14
4. 11, 12, 13, 14, 15, 16, 17, 18, 19, 20

Page 205
1. 5 + 5 = 10   2. 6 + 4 = 10   3. 4 + 5 = 9
4. 6 + 3 = 9   5. 6 + 6 = 12   6. 6 + 5 = 11
7. 4 + 4 = 8   8. 2 + 6 = 8   9. 6 + 0 = 6

10.
6 + 5 = 11

11.
6 + 6 = 12

12.
4 + 6 = 10

Page 206
1. 11   2. 11   3. 10   4. 8
5. 12   6. 12   7. 9   8. 11
9. 12   10. 11   11. 10   12. 12

Page 207
1. 8, 2   2. 4, 8
3. 9, 3   4. 6
5. 7, 5   6. 8, 3
7. 7, 4   8. 6, 5

Page 208
1. 6   2. 6   3. 4
4. 6   5. 8   6. 8
7. 8   8. 9   9. 5
10. 7   11. 7   12. 4

Page 209

Page 210

Page 211

1. _9_ (10 - 1) (2 + 7) (8 + 1) 3 + 5 11 - 3

2. _5_ 3 + 3 (6 - 1) 5 + 1 (5 + 0) (9 - 4)

3. _8_ (10 - 2) (4 + 4) 6 + 3 (2 + 6) 12 - 6

4. _10_ 12 - 3 (6 + 4) (7 + 3) 4 + 5 (11 - 1)

5. _12_ 4 + 7 (12 - 0) (8 + 4) (7 + 5) 6 + 5

6. _6_ (3 + 3) (12 - 6) (5 + 1) 9 + 3 11 - 4

7. _11_ 6 + 4 (9 + 2) (5 + 6) 7 + 5 (8 + 3)

8. _7_ (7 + 0) (11 - 4) (4 + 3) 2 + 6 12 - 1

Page 212

$12 - 9 = \underline{3}$ Brown
$10 - 9 = \underline{1}$ Red
$11 - 9 = \underline{2}$ Yellow
$12 - 8 = \underline{4}$ Green
$12 - 6 = \underline{6}$ Blue
$11 - 6 = \underline{5}$ Black

Page 213

1. 2, 5, 25
2. 2, 6, 26
3. 3, 8, 38
4. 3, 4, 34
5. 2, 8, 28
6. 3, 0, 30

Page 214

1. 5, 6, 56
2. 3, 2, 32
3. 4, 7, 47
4. 6, 8, 68

Page 215

1. 2 tens 6 ones _26_
2. 4 tens 1 one _41_
3. 7 tens 0 ones _70_
4. 5 tens 8 ones _58_
5. 6 tens 2 ones _62_
6. 8 tens 5 ones _85_
7. 3 tens 7 ones _37_

Page 216

	tens	ones		tens	ones
1.	2	5	2.	1	7
	4	3		7	1
	2	8		6	6
	3	0		1	9
	5	4		8	1
	6	5		4	0

Page 217

1	11	21	31	41	51	61	71	81	91
(2)	(12)	(22)	(32)	42	(52)	(62)	(72)	(82)	(92)
3	13	23	33	43	53	63	73	83	93
(4)	(14)	(24)	(34)	(44)	(54)	(64)	(74)	(84)	(94)
5	15	25	35	45	55	65	75	85	95
(6)	(16)	(26)	(36)	(46)	(56)	(66)	(76)	(86)	(96)
7	17	27	37	47	57	67	77	87	97
(8)	(18)	(28)	(38)	(48)	(58)	(68)	(78)	(88)	(98)
9	19	29	39	49	59	69	79	89	99
(10)	(20)	(30)	(40)	(50)	(60)	(70)	(80)	(90)	(100)

Page 218

1. 1, 2, 3, 4, 5, 6, 7, 8, 9, 10
2. 41, 42, 43, 44, 45, 46, 47, 48, 49, 50
3. 71, 72, 73, 74, 75, 76, 77, 78, 79, 80
4. 31, 32, 33, 34, 35, 36, 37, 38, 39, 40
5. 81, 82, 83, 84, 85, 86, 87, 88, 89, 90
6. 61, 62, 63, 64, 65, 66, 67, 68, 69
7. 91, 92, 93, 94, 95, 96, 97, 98, 99, 100

Page 219

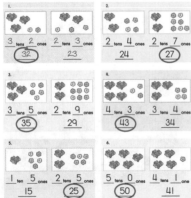

10   20   30   40   50
60   70   80   90   100

Page 220

1. _17_   2. 32
3. 23   4. 66
5. 80   6. 29
7. 44   8. 26
9. _23_   10. 12
11. 19   12. 38
13. 28   14. 7
15. 39   16. 70

Page 221

1. 3 tens 2 ones (32)   2 tens 3 ones 23
2. 2 tens 4 ones 24   2 tens 7 ones (27)
3. 3 tens 5 ones (35)   2 tens 9 ones 29
4. 4 tens 3 ones (43)   3 tens 4 ones 34
5. 1 ten 5 ones 15   2 tens 5 ones (25)
6. 5 tens 0 ones (50)   4 tens 1 one 41

Page 222

1. 23   2. 50   3. 31
4. 21   5. 35   6. 15
7. 18   8. 31   9. 43
10. 48   11. 25   12. 23
13. 59   14. 13   15. 25
16. 58   17. 44   18. 78

Page 223

1. 13   2. 14   3. 15   4. 12
5. 13   6. 14   7. 15   8. 12
9. 14   10. 12   11. 13   12. 11
13. 11   14. 9   15. 15   16. 10

Page 224
1. 13	**2.** 13	**3.** 12
4. 14	**5.** 12	**6.** 8
7. 15	**8.** 14	**9.** 14
10. 8	**11.** 6	**12.** 4
13. 6	**14.** 0	**15.** 7
16. 7	**17.** 8	**18.** 5

Page 225
1. 4	**2.** 4	**3.** 7
4. 6	**5.** 1	**6.** 7
7. 9	**8.** 7	**9.** 5
10. 9	**11.** 7	**12.** 7
13. 4	**14.** 0	**15.** 5
16. 8	**17.** 8	**18.** 9

Page 226
1. 12	**2.** 5	**3.** 15	**4.** 6
5. 3	**6.** 8	**7.** 13	**8.** 9
9. 15	**10.** 7	**11.** 6	**12.** 9
13. 9	**14.** 13	**15.** 0	**16.** 14

Page 227
1. 14	**2.** 15	**3.** 16	
4. 14	**5.** 15	**6.** 16	
7. 16	**8.** 17	**9.** 18	
10. 13	**11.** 13	**12.** 15	**13.** 11
14. 17	**15.** 16	**16.** 14	**17.** 18

Page 228

Page 229

+	0	1	2	3	4	5	6	7	8	9
0	0	1	2	3	4	5	6	7	8	9
1	1	2	3	4	5	6	7	8	9	10
2	2	3	4	5	6	7	8	9	10	11
3	3	4	5	6	7	8	9	10	11	12
4	4	5	6	7	8	9	10	11	12	13
5	5	6	7	8	9	10	11	12	13	14
6	6	7	8	9	10	11	12	13	14	15
7	7	8	9	10	11	12	13	14	15	16
8	8	9	10	11	12	13	14	15	16	17
9	9	10	11	12	13	14	15	16	17	18

1. 2	**2.** 4	**3.** 6
4. 8	**5.** 10	**6.** 12
7. 14	**8.** 16	**9.** 18

Page 230
1. 8, 9	**2.** 12, 13	**3.** 16, 17
4. 10, 11	**5.** 6, 7	**6.** 14, 15
7. 12, 13	**8.** 14, 15	
9. 10, 11	**10.** 16, 17	

Page 231
1. 9, 3	**2.** 9, 5	**3.** 8, 7
4. 8, 9	**5.** 8, 5	**6.** 5, 6

7. 8, 14 – 8 = 6
8. 9, 17 – 9 = 8
9. 3, 12 – 3 = 9
10. 8, 15 – 8 = 7
11. 9, 13 – 9 = 4
12. 6, 15 – 6 = 9

Page 232

Page 233
1. 11, 11, 7, 4
2. 16, 16, 9, 7
3. 7, 7, 7, 0
4. 13, 8, 8, 5
5. 17, 17, 17, 17
6. 18, 9

7. 6 + 9 = 15	**8.** 9 + 0 = 9	**9.** 5 + 7 = 12
9 + 6 = 15	0 + 9 = 9	7 + 5 = 12
15 – 6 = 9	9 – 0 = 9	12 – 5 = 7
15 – 9 = 6	9 – 9 = 0	12 – 7 = 5

Page 234
1. 11	**2.** 13	**3.** 17	**4.** 13	**5.** 10
6. 15	**7.** 12	**8.** 14	**9.** 17	**10.** 16

Page 235
1. 14
2. 17
3. 8
4. 0
5. 16

Page 236

Page 237

1. 9
2. 16
3. 2, 7, 27
4. 4, 1, 41
5. ⓔ23 33
6. 29 ㉟
7. ㊸ 34
8. 69 ㊲
9. 31, 32, 33, 34, 35, 36, 37, 38, 39, 40
10. 75, 76, 77, 78, 79, 80, 81, 82, 83, 84

Page 238

1. 11
2. 12
3. 18
4. 7
5. 17
6. 14
7. 5
8. 0
9. 7
10. 7
11. 9
12. 7
13. 7
14. 13
15. 8
16. 9
17. 12
18. 8
19. 16
20. 18
21. 7 + 9 = 16
9 + 7 = 16
16 − 7 = 9
16 − 9 = 7

Page 240

1. 5¢, 6¢, 7¢, 8¢
2. 5¢, 6¢, 7¢
3. 5¢, 6¢, 7¢, 8¢, 9¢
4. 5¢, 10¢

Page 241

1. 5¢, 10¢, 15¢, 20¢, 21¢, 22¢
2. 5¢, 6¢, 7¢, 8¢
3. 5¢, 10¢, 15¢, 16¢, 17¢
4. 5¢, 10¢, 11¢, 12¢, 13¢, 14¢

Page 242

1. 10¢
2. 11¢
3. 15¢
4. 14¢
5. 7¢
6. 18¢

Page 243

1. 10¢, 11¢, 12¢
2. 10¢, 11¢, 12¢ 13¢
3. 10¢, 11¢, 12¢ 13¢ 14¢ 15¢
4. 10¢, 11¢, 12¢ 13¢ 14¢ 15¢ 16¢

Page 244

1. 20¢
2. 21¢
3. 31¢
4. 22¢
5. 23¢
6. 60¢

Page 245

1. 10¢, 15¢, 16¢, 17¢
2. 10¢, 20¢, 25¢, 26¢
3. 10¢, 20¢, 25¢, 30¢, 35¢
4. 10¢, 20¢, 30¢, 35¢, 36¢, 37¢

Page 246

1. 50¢ no
2. 22¢ yes
3. 46¢ yes
4. 30¢ no
5. 22¢ yes
6. 18¢ no

Page 247

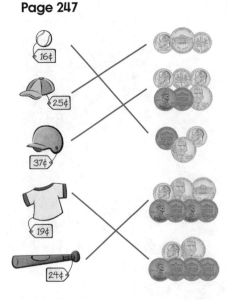

Page 248

1. 2 dimes, 2 pennies
2. 3 dimes, 1 penny
3. 1 dime, 1 nickel, 1 penny
4. 1 dime, 2 pennies
5. 2 dimes, 2 pennies
6. 3 dimes, 1 nickel

Page 249

1. 25¢, 26¢, 27¢ 28¢
2. 25¢, 35¢, 36¢ 37¢ 38¢
3. 25¢, 35¢, 40¢ 45¢
4. 25¢, 35¢, 45¢ 50¢ 51¢ 52¢

Page 250

1. 25¢, 35¢, 40¢ 41¢
2. 25¢, 30¢, 35¢ 36¢ 37¢
3. 25¢, 50¢, 60¢ 70¢ 75¢ 76¢
4. 25¢, 35¢, 45¢ 46¢ 47¢
5. 25¢, 50¢, 75¢ 80¢ 90¢

Page 251

1. 25¢
2. 25¢
3. 2̶8̶¢̶
4. 25¢
5. 25¢
6. 2̶4̶¢̶

Page 252

1.	32¢ + 50¢ 82¢	2.	44¢ + 24¢ 68¢
3.	44¢ + 15¢ 59¢	4.	63¢ + 32¢ 95¢
5.	63¢ + 24¢ 87¢	6.	15¢ + 50¢ 65¢

Page 253

60

Page 254
1. 3 o'clock; 3:00
2. 7 o'clock; 7:00
3. 9 o'clock; 9:00
4. 11 o'clock; 11:00
5. 8 o'clock; 8:00
6. 5 o'clock; 5:00

Page 255
1. Half past 4; 4:30
2. Half past 10; 10:30
3. Half past 6; 6:30
4. Half past 8; 8:30
5. Half past 12; 12:30
6. Half past 3; 3:30

Page 256
1. 4:00   2. 9:30   3. 1:30
4. 3:00   5. 8:30   6. 6:00

5:00 Cowboy Sam
5:30 Dinosaurs!
7:00 Joke Time
7:30 Camp Talk

Page 257
1. Quarter past 6; 6:15
2. Quarter past 8; 8:15
3. Quarter past 1; 1:15
4. Quarter past 12; 12:15
5. Quarter past 10; 10:15
6. Quarter past 7; 7:15

Page 258
1. Quarter to 12; 11:45
2. Quarter to 9; 8:45
3. Quarter to 1; 12:45
4. Quarter to 7; 6:45
5. Quarter to 2; 1:45
6. Quarter to 10; 9:45

Page 259
1. 2:15   2. 3:30   3. 4:30
4. 6:15   5. 6:00   6. 10:45
7. 8:45   8. 6:30   9. 12:00

Page 260
1. Fluffy
2. Toby
3. Pookie
4. Bailey
5. Squawk
6. Mia

Page 261
1. 1:45   2. 2:15   3. 7:45
4. 11:15   5. 3:45   6. 8:15

7.   8.   9.
   2:45   6:15   9:45

10. 11. 12.
   10:45   3:15   12:15

Page 262
1. 9:15   2. 6:00   3. 5:20
4. 10:45   5. 4:40   6. 11:30

7.   8.   9.
   3:50   12:00   7:15

10.   11.   12.
   12:50   8:30   2:45

Page 263
1. 10:15   2. 9:45   3. 4:15
4. 12:45   5. 8:15   6. 3:45

7. 8. 9.
   3:45   5:15   1:45

10. 11. 12.
   11:45   4:15   8:15

Page 264
1. 1:30   2. 6:00   3. 9:30
4. 10:30   5. 12:00   6. 5:30

7.   8.   9.
   6:30   8:00   1:00

10.   11.   12.
   11:30   5:00   2:30

ANSWER KEY

Page 265

1. 3:45
2. 2:45
3. 1:30
4. 6:00
5. 5:15
6. 4:30

Page 266

1. a.m.
2. p.m.
3. p.m.
4. a.m.
5. p.m.
6. a.m.

Page 267

1.
2.
3.
4.
5.
6.

Page 268

1.
2.
3.
4.
5.
6.
7.
8.
9.
10.
11.
12.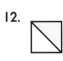

The $\frac{1}{2}$ section colored may vary.

Page 269

1.
2.
3.
4.
5.
6.
7.
8.
9.
10.
11.
12.

The $\frac{1}{3}$ section colored may vary.

Page 270

1.
2.
3.
4.
5.
6.
7.
8.
9.
10.
11.
12.

The $\frac{1}{4}$ section colored may vary.

Page 271

1. $\frac{1}{2}$ 2. $\frac{1}{3}$

3. $\frac{1}{4}$ 4. $\frac{1}{2}$

5. $\frac{1}{3}$ 6. $\frac{1}{4}$

Page 272

1. $\frac{2}{4}$ 2. $\frac{3}{4}$

3. $\frac{1}{2}$ 4. $\frac{4}{6}$

5. $\frac{3}{4}$ 6. $\frac{1}{3}$

Page 273

1.
2.
3.
4.
5.
6.
7.
8.
9.

Sections colored may vary. Please check your child's work.

Page 274
1. $\frac{1}{2}$ 2. $\frac{2}{3}$

3. $\frac{3}{4}$ 4. $\frac{5}{8}$

5. $\frac{3}{5}$ 6. $\frac{5}{6}$

7. $\frac{2}{5}$ 8. $\frac{1}{4}$

Page 275
1.   2.

3.   4.

5.   6.

7.   8.

Page 276
1. $\frac{1}{3}$ 2. $\frac{1}{2}$ 3. $\frac{1}{4}$

4. $\frac{1}{4}$ 5. $\frac{1}{3}$ 6. $\frac{1}{2}$

Page 279
1.   2.

3.   4.

5.   6.

7.   8.

Objects colored may vary. Please check your child's work.

Page 277
1.   2.

3.   4.

5.   6.

7.   8.

Page 278
1. 3 hats circled
2. 2 horses circled
3. 4 stars circled
4. 3 saddles circled
5. 5 horseshoes circled
6. 6 dogs circled

Page 280
1. 6
   +5
   ⎯⎯
   11 snowmen

2. 11
   −4
   ⎯⎯
   7 hats

3. 4
   +6
   ⎯⎯
   10 sleds

4. 11
   −5
   ⎯⎯
   6 cups

Page 281
1.   4 + 3 = 7

2.   7 − 3 = 4

3.   2 + 5 = 7

4.   6 − 2 = 4

5.   5 − 3 = 2

Page 282
1. How many dragonflies were left?
   6 − 3 = 3
2. How many butterflies were there in all?
   10 + 4 = 14
3. How many caterpillars were there in all?
   5 + 2 = 7
4. How many flies were left?
   8 − 7 = 1

Page 283
1. 5
   − 3
   ⎯⎯
   2 bees

2. 6
   − 4
   ⎯⎯
   2 bears

3. 6
   − 2
   ⎯⎯
   4 jars

Page 284
1. 7
   − 5
   ⎯⎯
   2 sheep

2. 8
   + 5
   ⎯⎯
   13 cows

3. 12
   − 4
   ⎯⎯
   8 eggs

Page 285
1. 34
   − 13
   ⎯⎯
   21 robins

2. 13
   + 11
   ⎯⎯
   24 tulips

3. 23
   + 14
   ⎯⎯
   37 butterflies

Page 286
1. 13
   + 6
   ⎯⎯
   19 pictures

2. 15
   − 8
   ⎯⎯
   7 fish

3. 14
   − 7
   ⎯⎯
   7 postcards

Page 287
1. 6
   − 4
   ⎯⎯
   2 piles of leaves

2. 8
   + 10
   ⎯⎯
   18 games

3. 16
   − 4
   ⎯⎯
   12 apples

Page 288
1. How many ladybugs were left?
   $10 - 5 = 5$
2. How many beetles are there in all?
   $11 + 3 = 14$
3. How many ants were there in all?
   $8 + 7 = 15$
4. How many bees were left?
   $12 - 3 = 9$

Page 294
1. 28
2. 30
3. Laura
4. Kayla
5. Laura, Bradley
6. Michael, Kayla
7. $\begin{array}{r} 33 \\ + 30 \\ \hline 63 \end{array}$ 8. $\begin{array}{r} 40 \\ - 28 \\ \hline 12 \end{array}$

Page 289
1. 6
2. 7
3. 8
4. Bret
5. Zach
6. $9 + 4 = 13$
7. $6 + 7 = 13$
8. $8 - 6 = 2$

Page 290
1. 4
2. 5
3. 3
4. 2
5. 6
6. 5
7. $3 + 5 = 8$
8. $6 - 4 = 2$

Page 291
1. 7
2. 4
3. $4 + 2 = 6$
4. $8 + 2 = 10$
5. $8 - 4 = 4$
6. $4 + 7 = 11$

Page 292
1. 6
2. 10
3. 8
4. $8 - 6 = 2$
5. $10 - 6 = 4$
6. $6 + 8 = 14$

Page 293
1. 3
2. 5
3. 6
4. Dog
5. Pony
6. $10 - 6 = 4$
7. $5 + 6 = 11$

Page 295
1.

Sunday	Monday	Tuesday	Wednesday	Thursday	Friday	Saturday
		1	2	3	4	5
6	7	8	9	10	11	12
13	14	15	16	17	18	19
20	21	22	23	24	25	26
27	28	29	30			

June

2. Wednesday
3. Thursday
4. Tuesday
5. June 7
6. June 11
7. 7
8. $7 + 7 = 14$
9. 30

Page 296
1.

Sunday	Monday	Tuesday	Wednesday	Thursday	Friday	Saturday
				1	2	3
4	5	6	7	8	9	10
11	12	13	14	15	16	17
18	19	20	21	22	23	24
25	26	27	28	29	30	31

December

2. Saturday
3. Wednesday
4. December 14
5. December 19
6. $7 + 7 + 7 = 21$
7. 31
8. December 20
9. December 18

Page 297
1. $\begin{array}{r} 45 \\ - 30 \\ \hline 15 \text{ minutes} \end{array}$
2. $\begin{array}{r} 25 \\ - 10 \\ \hline 15 \text{ minutes} \end{array}$
3. $\begin{array}{r} 30 \\ + 15 \\ \hline 45 \text{ minutes} \end{array}$

Page 298
1. 4:30
2. 2:00
3. 3:30
4. 9:00

Page 299
1. 3:20
2. 7:05
3. 5:00
4. 11:15

Page 300
1. "Her sister is 8 years old." should be crossed out.
   $\begin{array}{r} 12 \\ - 5 \\ \hline 7 \text{ years} \end{array}$
2. "Alex bought 7 gifts." should be crossed out.
   $\begin{array}{r} 8 \\ + 5 \\ \hline 13 \text{ gifts} \end{array}$

Page 301
1. "Taylor weighs 67 pounds." should be crossed out.
   $\begin{array}{r} 72 \\ + 65 \\ \hline 137 \text{ pounds} \end{array}$
2. "Ellie's father is 35 years old." and "Ellie is 8 years old." should be crossed out.
   $\begin{array}{r} 39 \\ + 30 \\ \hline 69 \text{ years old} \end{array}$

Page 302
1. Ben
2. Sue
3. Bob
4. Al
5. Joe

3. "Mark has 10 pizza slices." and "Jose has 9 pizza slices." should be crossed out.
   $\begin{array}{r} 7 \\ - 5 \\ \hline 2 \text{ pizza slices} \end{array}$